THE SIGN:
A PERSONAL STUDY GUIDE

• ROBERT VAN KAMPEN •
• REVEREND ROGER BEST •

CROSSWAY BOOKS • WHEATON, ILLINOIS
A DIVISION OF GOOD NEWS PUBLISHERS

The Sign: A Personal Study Guide

Copyright ©1994 Robert Van Kampen and Roger Best

Published by Crossway Books, a division of
Good News Publishers, 1300 Crescent Street, Wheaton, Illinois 60187

Cover illustration: Michael Carroll

First printing, 1994

Printed in the United States of America

ISBN 0-89107-757-X

All Bible quotations, unless otherwise indicated, are taken from *New American Standard Bible,*
copyright ©1977 by the Lockman Foundation.

T A B L E   O F
CONTENTS

THE
INTRODUCTION

The question that has been on the minds and hearts of Christians through the centuries is, "When is Jesus coming back?" Among genuine believers the question has never been "If the Lord Jesus returns?" but "When will the Lord Jesus return for His own?" From the very early days of the Church, believers were longing for and looking for the return of Christ.

Today, as in the past, every believer who truly loves the Lord also longs for the return of Christ. Yet in most evangelical churches today there is much confusion concerning the second coming of Christ. But this does not have to be the case. We can, in fact, have a clear understanding of the end times and the monumental events that the Lord has in store!

How can we have this confidence? The key is to see what God's Word so clearly teaches—instead of relying on tradition, man-made theological systems, allegorical interpretation, past teachers, or anything else. The answer lies in the careful study of Scripture, using basic rules of proper interpretation. And when we do this, the Scriptures come alive, and the answers, in effect, seem to jump off the page.

The purpose of this study workbook, then, is to help each reader to gain a deeper understanding of God's Word and to have an absolute confidence in what the Scriptures teach concerning the return of Christ. Two questions are of critical importance in this regard. First, can we, in fact, know and understand the sequence of events surrounding the Second Coming of Christ? And second, why is the timing of Christ's return so important?

To answer these questions let us consider what the Word of God says. First, let us look at Christ's response to the question of His disciples in Matthew 24:3 where they ask, "What will be the sign of Your coming and the end of the age?" Verse 4 tells us that Jesus answers their question with this warning. "See to it that no one misleads you." Then again, when there was confusion in the church concerning the second coming of Christ, Paul tells the believers in Thessalonica exactly when Christ's return will take place—but first He warns them to "Let no one in any way deceive you" (2 Thessalonians 2:3). Peter affirms the same truth in 2 Peter 1:16, "For we did not follow cleverly devised tales when we made known to you the power and coming of Jesus Christ, but we were eyewitnesses of His majesty." Similarly, like Christ and Paul before him, Peter also warns his readers concerning the events that surround the 2nd coming of Christ, and goes on in verse 20 to give the primary reason for the overwhelming confusion concerning prophecy of Christ's second coming: "But know this first of all, that no prophecy of Scripture is a matter of one's own interpretation."

In other words, Peter explains that the confusion concerning Christ's return typically results from "one's own interpretation"—that is, from individuals who develop mistaken system of interpretation and then teach such systems to vast members of followers. That is why so much confusion exists today. But the teaching of the New Testament has not changed in 2,000 years, and the truth concerning the 2nd coming of Christ is the same today as it was in the days the teaching was inspired by God. It is for this reason that Paul, in 2 Thessalonians 3:14,15, gives such a strong warning to believers in regard to his teaching concerning the return of Christ in this epistle. "And if anyone does not obey our instruction in this letter, take special note of that man and do not associate with him, so that he may be put to shame. And yet do not regard him as an enemy, but admonish him as a brother."

We need to heed Paul's exhortation to faithful believers in 1 Thessalonians 5:6 "not [to] sleep as others do, but ... [to] be alert and sober"—so that we will not be like the unsuspecting world for whom Christ's coming will be like a thief in the night.

It is our prayer and desire that this study guide will help you in your understanding of the Scriptures, especially as it pertains to the 2nd coming of Christ, and that you will gain a deep sense of understanding concerning the clear teaching of God's Word on the great hope of the church.

To make this study profitable you will need your Bible, a copy of the book *The Sign*, and an open heart before God. (**Note:** the page reference numbers are based on the Expanded Edition of *The Sign*. For ease in using the Study Guide the reader should be sure to use the Expanded Edition of *The Sign* for this study.)

KEY PROPHETIC PASSAGES

Listed below are a number of *Key Prophetic Verses* that will be a great source of help for you to be acquainted with in your pursuit of understanding what God's Word says to us concerning the end time events. It would be helpful to be familiar with a few of these immediately as you begin this study, and we would encourage you to read those with an asterisk even now as you begin.

This list will also serve as a helpful reference as you work through this study—to read and compare the Scripture for a deeper and clearer understanding of how the many prophetic passages in the Bible are in complete harmony and provide a comprehensive picture of prophetic truth.

OLD TESTAMENT

Daniel 2
Daniel 7
Daniel 9:11-27
Daniel 11:36 - 12:13
Ezekiel 20:33-44
Ezekiel 37-39
Zechariah 12-14
Isaiah 2, 24-28, 65,66
Zephaniah 1
Joel 2:31 - 3:17
Hosea 5:8 - 6:3

NEW TESTAMENT

Matthew 13:24-43
Matthew 24-25*
Luke 17:22 - 18:8
Luke 21
Romans 11:11-26
1 Thessaloanians 4:13 - 5:11*
2 Thessalonians 1-2*
1 Peter 4:7-18*
2 Peter 2:4 - 3:17*
Revelation

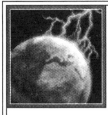

CHAPTER-BY-CHAPTER STUDY

We would encourage you to use this workbook to study *The Sign* a chapter at a time. Probably the most effective approach is to use the following steps in studying each chapter:

1. Pray that the Lord would enlighten your heart and your mind as you seek to know His truth as revealed in His Word.

2. Read the chapter through. Take special note of the Scripture passages referred to. Take notes and underline key points.

3. Go through the chapter in the workbook question by question—with your Bible in hand and your copy of *The Sign* ready for reference and clarification.

4. Try to answer each question first without looking up the answers in the back of the Study Guide. If, however, you have difficulty with a question, feel free to refer to the answers in the back, <u>but</u> also study the answer and compare with Scripture to be sure that you clearly understand yourself.

5. When you have finished the chapter, go back and review the answers in the workbook to gain a clearer sense of the central themes and truths.

6. Pray that the Lord would apply these truths to your life as you seek to live faithfully for Him—especially as the last days seem to be approaching so rapidly.

KEY TERMS NECESSARY FOR UNDERSTANDING PROPHETIC SCRIPTURE

It will be extremely helpful in your study to refer often to the glossary and the endnotes of *The Sign*. They are placed there to help you have a clear understanding of the arguments presented. Before embarking on this study, careful study in the glossary of the following terms will help you immensely in your understanding of *The Sign*.

Antichrist
Armageddon, Battle of (or Campaign)
Beast, the
Beast Empire, the Final (Eighth)
Birth Pangs, Beginning of
Bowl Judgments
Bride of Christ, the
Christ, Second Coming
Church in General, the
Church, the True
Day of the Lord
Gentiles, Time (or Fullness) of
Imminency, the Doctrine of
Kingdom of God

Kingdom of God, the Physical
Kingdom of God, the Spiritual
Millennium, the
Olivet Discourse
Pretribulationism
Prewrath Rapture
Rapture, the
Seals of Revelation, the Seven
Seventieth Week
Sign of Christ's coming (or of the Son of Man), the
Sign of the End of the Age, the
Testing, the Time of
Tribulation
Tribulation, the Great
Trumpet Judgments, the Seven
Trumpet, the Seventh
Wrath, God's

Lastly, we would pray that the Lord would enlighten your heart and your mind as you seek to know His Truth concerning the return of Christ. May the Lord be with you and give you confidence, assurance, and perseverance as you prepare for the momentous last days and look forward to that great day when Christ shall return in power and great glory.

CHAPTER
ONE

FOUNDATIONS FOR
UNDERSTANDING PROPHETIC TRUTH

F **CHAPTER FOCUS:**

The first chapter gives you the foundations necessary for understanding the prophetic truth of the Word of God. In this chapter you will be introduced to the most common positions concerning the return of Christ and the areas of disagreement that have produced major division within the church, today. You will learn the importance of a proper hermeneutic (interpretation) for your individual study of God's Word and you will be introduced to the prewrath position concerning the coming of Jesus Christ that, as you will quickly recognize, flows naturally from the use of a literal hermeneutic.

R **Read Chapter 1 of *The Sign* before answering the following questions.**

MAJOR DISAGREEMENTS

1-1 Among Bible-believing Christians, what are the three major areas of disagreement in relationship to the return of Christ? (p. 25)

1.

2.

3.

THE COMING PERSECUTION

1-2 According to Romans 5:9, 1 Thessalonians 1:10 and 2 Thessalonians 5:9, what will happen to the true church (genuine Christians) before the wrath of God is meted out upon the earth? (pp. 25-26)

1-3 Is persecution ever to be part of the Christian experience? (pp. 26-27)

1-4 According to the prewrath position, how does it harmonize the two preceding questions? (p. 27)

PRINCIPLES OF INTERPRETATION

1-5 What are the five principles of interpretation that are used by the author? (pp. 27-29)

1.

2.

3.

4.

5.

1-6 What is an "antinomy?" (p. 29)

1-7 In relation to a given prophetic event or issue, why should we carefully study and compare various texts in both the Old and New Testaments? (p. 30)

1-8 According to Daniel 12:4,9, prophecy will be sealed up until the end times. What great advantage does the modern student of prophecy have over those of days gone by? (pp. 30-31)

THE PIVOTAL TEXTS

1-9 What are the two pivotal New Testament texts given primarily for the believer's understanding of end-time events? (pp. 31-32)

1-10 What makes the Olivet Discourse (Matthew 24,25) and the book of Revelation so pivotal? (p. 32)

THE VARIOUS POSITIONS CONCERNING CHRIST'S RETURN

1-11 What are the basic tenets of the pretribulational rapture position? (p. 32)

1-12 Is the seventieth week of Daniel ever called the "tribulation period" anywhere in Scripture? (p. 32)

1-13 What is the origin of the "pretribulational" Rapture position? (pp. 32, 461-462 end note 1)

1-14 What is the amillennial position concerning Christ's return, and what is its distinct approach to end times? (p. 33)

THE PREWRATH POSITION

1-15 What is the prewrath position concerning the timing of the Rapture? (p. 34)

1-16 Why is the prewrath position and the position of the early church fathers so similar? (pp. 33, 463-465 endnote 3)

1-17 Who were some of the early church fathers who taught that the church would face the onslaught of Antichrist? (p. 465)

1-18 What caused the church to move away from this position after A.D. 325? (p. 467)

THE DOCTRINE OF IMMINENCY

1-19 Explain the doctrine of "imminency" as it pertains to the second coming of Christ. (p. 442 - Glossary)

1-20 Did any of the early church fathers teach imminence, the doctrine of an "any moment" return of Christ? (p. 467 endnote 3)

THE IMPORTANCE OF THE PREWRATH POSITION

1-21 If a Christian's view of end-time events does not affect his salvation, why is it important? (p. 36)

THE PURPOSE OF THIS BOOK

1-22 What is the purpose of this book? (p. 37)

1-23 What is the author's desire for God's children as a result of this book? (p. 36)

1-24 According to 1 Thessalonians 5:4-6, do Christians have any excuse for being taken by surprise in the end times? (p. 37)

Personal Notes & Quotes:

A WARNING TO THE CHURCH

F **CHAPTER FOCUS:**

In this chapter you will gain a better understanding of the seven churches of Asia Minor that the book of Revelation was addressed to, and see the near/far prophetic implications to those of the true church of Christ that will go into the last days of the end times. You will also begin to see why it is so vitally important for every believer to be faithful and prepared for the end times.

R **Read chapter 2 of *The Sign* before answering the following questions.**

2-1 Why is it vitally important for the believer to be prepared for the end times? (p. 39)

....

....

THE SEVEN CHURCHES OF REVELATION

2-2 What is the book of Revelation all about? (p. 40)

....

2-3 Who is the direct source of the instruction found in the book of Revelation? (p. 40)

....

2-4 According to Revelation 1:3 and 22:16, who is the book of Revelation directed to? (p. 40)

....

....

2-5 Why do the seven churches of Revelation chapters 2-3 depict the condition of the church just preceding the end of the age? (pp. 40-41)

THREE REPRESENTATIVE TYPES OF CHURCHES

2-6 The seven churches can be grouped into three basic types that will characterize the church (or Christians, individually) at the time of the return of Christ. What are the three basic types of churches represented, and which church described in Revelation best represents each of these types? (p. 41)

1.

2.

3.

Note: It should be noted that references to dead, faithful and compromising churches are references to not only the church itself, but also to the individuals that comprise the church in general. In other words, a faithful church will be made up primarily of faithful Christians but may also include both dead and compromising individuals that attend as well. This is an important principle to remember as one works throughout this teaching manual.

THE FAITHFUL CHURCH

2-7 What is the promise given to the "faithful church" in Revelation 3:10? (p. 41)

2-8 Is the translation "keep you from" the best and most common translation of the Greek words "tereo ek?" (pp. 42, 467-469 endnote 1)

2-9 Give the most accurate and common definition of the Greek verb "tereo." (pp. 42, 467 endnote 1)

2-10 Using the same endnote as used in the preceding question, now give the most accurate and common definition of the Greek word "ek." How does this more accurate definition of "ek" affect our key passage found in Revelation 3:10? (p. 467 endnote 1)

2-11 Now, putting together the most accurate and common translations of the two critical Greek words we have just worked through, what then is the best English translation of "tereo ek" as used in Revelation 3:10? (p. 42)

2-12 Comparing Scripture with Scripture, in what other passage is "tereo ek" used in a similar way? (p. 468 endnote 1)

2-13 What exactly is the sphere of danger that most conservative scholars believe the faithful church will be given protection from? (p. 42)

2-14 What is the underlying idea behind the word "testing" in its context of Revelation 3:10, "the hour of testing?" (p. 469 endnote 2)

2-15 What time during the end times do most conservative scholars agree that the "hour of testing" is referring to? (p. 469 endnote 2)

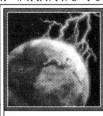

2-16 What important truth do we find in Peter's use of the same Greek word, "peirasmos," in 1 Peter 4:12 and 2 Peter 2:9? (p. 470 endnote 2)

2-17 In summary then, what does Christ mean in Revelation 3:10 when He promises the faithful believer He will "tereo ek" the faithful during "the hour of testing?" (p. 42)

2-18 What are the three main characteristics that characterize the faithful church during the end times? (p. 43)

1.

2.

3.

2-19 From Revelation 3:11, how do we know that the prophecy concerning the Philadelphia church is an end-time prophecy?

THE DEAD CHURCH

2-20 What is the condition of the church at Sardis? (p. 43)

2-21 According to the "wheat and tare" parable of Christ recorded in Matthew 13:24-30, what can the church of Sardis be compared to?

2-22 What is the future of the church at Sardis? (p. 44)

2-23 What are the two major characteristics of the spiritually dead church? (p. 44)

    1.

    2.

2-24 How does Christ's illustration of some "taken" and others "left," recorded in Matthew 24:36-41, have application to the church in hiding, during the days of persecution by Antichrist?

2-25 What parable of Christ given in His Olivet Discourse as recorded in Matthew, further substantiates this fact?

2-26 In Revelation 3:3 Christ warns the church of Sardis that if they do not wake up, "I will come like a thief." Where else in Scripture do we see the terminology "thief in the night," and to what does it refer? (p. 44)

2-27 Again, according to Revelation 3:3, how do we know that this prophecy concerning the church of Sardis is an end-time prophecy?

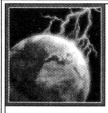

THE COMPROMISING CHURCH

2-28 Using the church at Thyatira as an example of compromising Christians in the last days, why does it best characterize the church in general, just before the end times? (p. 44)

2-29 According to Revelation 2:20, what is the foremost problem in this church? (p. 45)

2-30 What is the lesson being taught here? (p. 45)

2-31 What does Revelation 2:22 reveal will happen to the "bond servants" within the compromising church? (p. 46)

2-32 In Revelation 2:22 Christ uses the term "great tribulation." How many other times is this term used in the New Testament, and where?

2-33 Comparing Scripture with Scripture, who is the only person who uses (or causes to be used) the term, "great tribulation"?

2-34 Do these two other passages, other than the passage concerning the church of Thyatira, speak of any thing other than the "great tribulation" of Antichrist?

2-35 Comparing Scripture with Scripture, then, what can be our only conclusion concerning the use of the same term "great tribulation" in the Thyatira context?

2-36 What is an especially important fact to note in Revelation 2:23 about the church in general? (p. 46)

2-37 Why will the compromising church be required to face the persecution of Antichrist? (p. 47)

2-38 How do we specifically know from Revelation 2:25 that, once again, the warning to the church of Thyatira is also an end-time prophecy?

THREE ESSENTIAL TRUTHS

2-39 In summary, what is the essential truth we learn about the faithful church (true Christians) that will enter the last days? (p. 48)

2-40 What is the essential truth we learn about the spiritually dead church (false Christians) that will enter the last days? (p. 48)

2-41 And, what is the essential truth we learn about the compromising church (unfaithful Christians) that will enter the last days? (p. 48)

2-42 In looking at the example of Sodom and Gomorrah in Genesis 18:17-19, why is it important that Christians live godly lives as we look for His return? (pp. 48-49)

THREE CONCLUDING CONCERNS

2-43 What are three urgent, concluding concerns given at the end of this chapter? (p. 50)

1.

2.

3.

CHAPTER THREE

THE COSMIC CONFLICT

F **CHAPTER FOCUS:**

In this chapter you will be given an overview of the conflict that has waged down through the ages between good and evil — the kingdom of God against the kingdom of Satan. You will also see our sovereign God's plan for the redemption of His chosen ones from the kingdom of Satan into the kingdom of God. You will look at the tremendous truths associated with the first coming of Jesus Christ and finally, Satan's continuous battle to thwart God's plan for the ages.

R **Read chapter 3 of *The Sign* before answering the following questions.**

GOD'S SOVEREIGNTY

3-1 When did the cosmic conflict between God and Satan begin? (p. 52)

3-2 Why is this conflict not a contest? (p. 52)

3-3 Explain the two spiritual kingdoms that have existed since the conflict began. (p. 53)

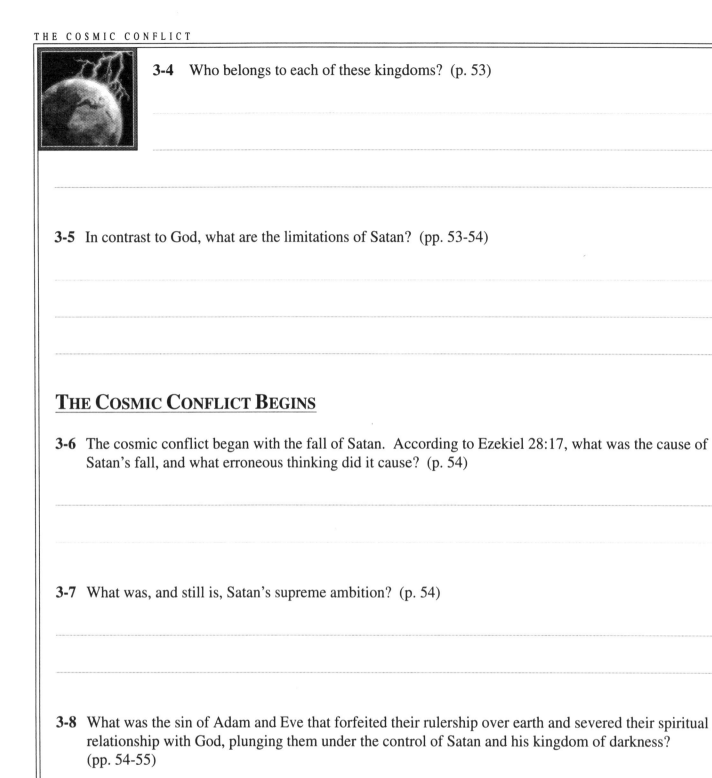

3-4 Who belongs to each of these kingdoms? (p. 53)

3-5 In contrast to God, what are the limitations of Satan? (pp. 53-54)

THE COSMIC CONFLICT BEGINS

3-6 The cosmic conflict began with the fall of Satan. According to Ezekiel 28:17, what was the cause of Satan's fall, and what erroneous thinking did it cause? (p. 54)

3-7 What was, and still is, Satan's supreme ambition? (p. 54)

3-8 What was the sin of Adam and Eve that forfeited their rulership over earth and severed their spiritual relationship with God, plunging them under the control of Satan and his kingdom of darkness? (pp. 54-55)

3-9 According to Romans 5:12 and 8:20, was the consequence of their sin limited to only Adam and Eve? (p. 55)

3-10 According to Genesis 2:17, what was the primary result of Adam's sin? (p. 54)

3-11 What is death? (p. 54)

3-12 Two different deaths came about as the direct result of Adam's sin. What is the first death and its consequences? (p. 55)

3-13 What is the second death? (p. 55)

3-14 Look at John 12:31; 14:30; 16:11; 2 Corinthians 4:4; and Ephesians 2:1,2 and tell what Satan accomplished by leading man into sin? (p. 55)

3-15 According to Genesis 3:15, how did God make known to Satan that his rule over mankind was temporary?

GOD'S PROPHETIC PLAN

Note: Before we can begin to understand God's prophetic plan for the ages, several definitions must be clearly understood. For this reason, please check and understand the definitions (described in the Glossary) of the following terms: Kingdom of God; Kingdom of God, the Spiritual; Kingdom of God, the Physical; Israel, the Natural Line of; Abraham, the Spiritual Descendants of; and Abraham, the Natural Descendants of. These are critical terms and should be fully understood before this study continues, as reference to them will be made repeatedly throughout our study together.

3-16 In God's sovereign prophetic plan for the overthrow of Satan's dominion over earth, what was <u>the first step</u>? (p. 56)

Note: Those He chose eventually become the citizens of the kingdom of God, each specifically at that point in life of their individual salvation.

3-17 Who does the natural line of Abraham refer to? (p. 57)

3-18 Using Romans 9:6-8, 11:11, and Galations 3:29, explain the inter-relationship between the natural and spiritual lines of Abraham. (p. 58)

3-19 What was <u>the second step</u> in God's sovereign prophetic plan for the overthrow of Satan, and why is it so important? (p. 58)

3-20 What was <u>the third step</u>, and why was this necessary? (p. 59)

3-21 What will be the fourth step? (p. 60)

3-22 What will be the fifth step, and when will it take place? (p. 61)

3-23 What will be the sixth and final step in God's plan for the overthrow of Satan's dominion over earth, and how does it tie into the blowing of the seventh trumpet described in Revelation 11:15-17? (pp. 62-63)

CHRIST'S FIRST COMING

3-24 What was the first accomplishment of Christ's first coming? (p. 64)

3-25 What was the second accomplishment? (p. 64)

3-26 What was the third accomplishment? (p. 64)

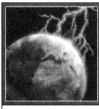

3-27 According to John 12:31, what was the fourth accomplishment of Christ's first coming? (p. 64)

CHRIST'S SECOND COMING

3-28 According to Luke 17:26-30, what will be the first major objective of Christ's second coming? (p. 65)

3-29 According to 2 Peter 3:3-7, what will be the second major objective? (p. 66)

3-30 According to Zechariah 12:10 and 13:9, what will be the third major objective? (p. 66)

3-31 What will be the fourth major objective of Christ's second coming? (p. 66)

SATAN'S COUNTERATTACK

Note: Blinded by his unbounded pride, Satan, the ruler of the kingdom of darkness, has his own counter-strategy to ward off the prophetic plan of God for his overthrow.

DESTROY OR DISQUALIFY THE LINE OF CHRIST

3-32 What was the first strategy of Satan, and how did he attempt to carry it out? (pp. 67-68)

3-33 According to Romans 11:2-5, was Satan successful in his mission to deceive or completely destroy the natural line of Abraham?

3-34 Based upon Revelation 13:1,2, what term does the author use when referring to these "elect nations of Satan?" (p. 69)

3-35 According to Revelation 17:10,11, how many beast empires will Satan use from start to finish? (p. 69)

DESTROY OR DISQUALIFY CHRIST

3-36 After failing at his first strategy, what was <u>Satan's second strategy</u>? (p. 69)

3-37 According to Hebrews 4:15, was Satan successful?

3-38 What significant event took place, according to Matthew 4:8-9, with end-time implications for each of us? (pp. 70-71)

DESTROY THE SUBJECTS OF CHRIST'S KINGDOM

3-39 Because of Satan's failure to disqualify Christ, against whom will he direct his final attack? (p. 72)

3-40 According to Daniel 10:21 and 12:1, who has been the one God has assigned to protect Israel? (p. 72)

3-41 According to Revelation 12:12, 17, who will be the primary target of Antichrist in the last days? (p. 73)

3-42 Using the same passage as in the question above, who will be Satan's secondary target? (p. 73)

3-43 According to Romans 4:9-11 and Galatians 3:29, who are "the rest of her offspring?"

3-44 What are true believers called in Revelation 13:7?

THE FINAL CONFLICT

3-45 When does the final conflict begin and end, and what is its ultimate outcome? (pp. 74-75)

CHAPTER
FOUR

THE BLESSINGS AND THE CURSES

F **CHAPTER FOCUS:**

In this chapter you will learn the all-important biblical principle that with obedience comes blessing and with disobedience, cursing. This is the principle that has driven God's relationship with Israel from the beginning and will continue to be the basis of God's relationship with them, as well as the church, in the last days.

R **Read chapter 4 of *The Sign* before answering the following questions.**

4-1 What is the nature and purpose of God's law as given in the Scriptures? (p. 77)

THE BLESSINGS OF OBEDIENCE

4-2 What is the significance of Leviticus 26:3-7, 9, 11? (p. 78)

THE CONSEQUENCES OF DISOBEDIENCE

4-3 According to Leviticus 26:14-25, 27-32, if blessings come with obedience, then what did God warn Israel would be the consequences of continued disobedience, and in what sequence? (pp. 79-80)

4-4 According to Leviticus 26:33, 38,39, what would be the ultimate curse against Israel?

4-5 According to Leviticus 26:43,44, will the ultimate curse ever become a reality?

4-6 What provision had God made beforehand for Israel? (p. 80)

4-7 How did Israel respond to God's warning concerning the blessings and the curses which would come as a direct result of Israel's behavior? (pp. 80-81)

4-8 Paralleling the Leviticus account, what was the ultimate curse recorded in Deuteronomy 28:64-66?

THE GREAT DIASPORA

4-9 What would cause the final, ultimate curse, and when in history did the ultimate curse take place? (p. 82)

4-10 How does the prophet Zechariah in 13:7, warn Israel concerning the rejection of their Messiah?

4-11 What do we know this curse as today? (p. 82)

THE RESTORATION OF ISRAEL

4-12 The Great Diaspora was not the end for Israel. What four things will yet take place for Israel according to Deuteronomy 30:1, 5-9? (pp. 84-85)

1.

2.

3.

4.

WHEN WILL THESE THINGS HAPPEN

4-13 According to Matthew 24:32-36, 42, does God give us any idea when Christ will come and these things will take place? (pp. 85-86)

Personal Notes & Quotes:

CHAPTER FIVE

THE "SEVENTY WEEK" PROPHETIC TIMETABLE

F **CHAPTER FOCUS:**

This chapter will give you the absolutely necessary understanding (for your understanding of the end times) of Daniel's critical prophecy of seventy weeks. You will understand why the seventy weeks really represent 490 years and who God is dealing with during the seventy weeks. This chapter will also help you to understand the gap between the sixty-ninth and seventieth week, as it relates to the Great Diaspora discussed in the last chapter.

R **Read chapter 5 of *The Sign* before answering the following questions.**

THE SEVENTY WEEKS OF DANIEL

5-1 What do the "seventy weeks" of Daniel refer to, as to actual time periods, when Daniel 12:7, 11-12 is compared with Revelation 11:2,3; 12:6, 14; and 13:5? (p. 88)

5-2 How many days are there in a prophetic year? (p. 87)

5-3 The focus of our critical prophetic passage is found in Daniel 9:24. Who and what is the focal point of Daniel's prophecy? (p. 88)

5-4 Again in Daniel 9:24, what two critical prophetic truths is Gabriel giving Daniel concerning Israel and their holy city, Jerusalem? (p. 89)

5-5 According to Romans 11:25 and Luke 21:24, what other two names are given to this time of Gentile domination?

5-6 What does "everlasting righteousness" mean in the context of Daniel 9:24 when compared to Romans 11:25,26?

5-7 How does Romans 11:25,26 tie together these two critical prophetic events (see question 5-4) that are recorded in Daniel 9:24?

5-8 When did the seventy weeks begin? (p. 89)

Note: This is an important prophecy to understand and an incredible argument to use when dealing with unsaved Jewish friends concerning the Messiahship of Jesus Christ.

5-9 What is the significance of the sequence of events outlined in Daniel 9:24-27? (p. 90)

5-10 In the sequence of events regarding the seventy weeks (490 years), where are we now? (p. 90)

5-11 According to Daniel 12:11,12, what specific part of the final seventieth week is detailed for us in this passage, and how do we come to this conclusion? (pp. 89-90)

5-12 When do the additional seventy-five days occur? (pp. 89-90)

WHY THE LONG GAP?

5-13 With the 483 years (the first 69 weeks) being completed on Palm Sunday, according to Daniel 9:26, what two critical events had to then occur before the beginning of the seventieth week, outlined in verse 27, could commence?

5-14 When did these two events occur in relationship to Palm Sunday?

5-15 According to Daniel 9:27, what is the event that will initiate the seventieth week of Daniel's prophecy, and according to verse 24, what will the completion of this specific seven-year period "bring in"?

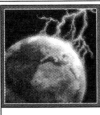

5-16 Almost two thousand years later, have either of these two critical events occurred yet, to date?

5-17 What does the author call this particular time period between the end of the sixty-ninth week and the beginning of the seventieth week?

5-18 According to Romans 11:11 why did the gap take place? (p. 92).

5-19 Because the gap has lasted so many centuries, how do we know for sure that God has not forgotten Israel (see Romans 11:1,2; 11,12; 20,21; 24-26)? (pp. 92-93)

5-20 Comparing Romans 11:25,26 with Daniel 9:24, when will the fullness of the Gentiles come in?

5-21 According to Romans 11:11-24, what is God doing for the Gentiles during the gap, and why? (p. 93)

5-22 According to chapter 3 (of The Sign), point 5 of God's sovereign plan concerning Israel, what is Satan's dilemma in response to God's promise to Israel?

THE SEVENTIETH WEEK

5-23 According to the following passages, what will Satan do in the seventieth week, (Daniel 7:7,8; 9:27; 12:1; Matthew 24:15, 21,22)? (pp. 93-94)

5-24 What significant events have taken place that allow us to look forward to the end of the age with a sense of expectancy and urgency as never before? (p. 95)

5-25 What is the next and last event that must take place before the seventieth week can begin? (p. 95)

Personal Notes & Quotes:

CHAPTER
SIX

THE FIRST SEVEN BEAST EMPIRES

F **CHAPTER FOCUS:**

This chapter will introduce to you and identify for you, the seven beast empires of Satan that Satan has used in the past in his attempt to destroy the nation of Israel, the natural line of Abraham.

R **Read chapter 6 of *The Sign* before answering the following questions.**

6-1 According to Revelation 17:3 and Daniel 7:3, how does Scripture refer to the nations that align themselves with Satan? (p. 97)

_____

_____

6-2 What is the significance of the beast empires? (p. 97)

_____

_____

THE EIGHT BEAST EMPIRES INTRODUCED

6-3 According to Revelation 17:10, who do the "seven heads" of Revelation 17:3 represent? (p. 98)

_____

6-4 According to Revelation 17:12, who do the "ten horns" of that same passage represent? (p. 98)

_____

6-5 According to Revelation 17:9-12, who will rule the 8th beast empire, and where will this ruler of this final beast empire come from? (p. 98)

THE BEAST EMPIRES OF NEBUCHADNEZZAR'S DREAM

6-6 Which beast empires are seen in Nebuchadnezzar's dream in Daniel 2:31-35, 37-44? (pp. 99-100)

6-7 With which "beast empire" does the seventy weeks begin? (p. 104)

THE BEAST EMPIRES OF DANIEL'S VISION

6-8 What is the correlation between the beast empires in Daniel's vision in Daniel 2:2-8 and in Nebuchadnezzar's dream of the statue? (p. 101)

1.

2.

3.

4.

THE FIRST SIX BEAST EMPIRES IDENTIFIED

6-9 Why is it important to properly identify the first six beast empires? (p. 101)

CHAPTER 6 SIX

6-10 What does the table of nations in Genesis 10 have to do with the last days? (p. 102)

6-11 What is the most striking characteristic of all the beast empires? (p. 102)

6-12 Who are the first six beast empires and from whom in the table of nations are they descended? (pp. 102-104)

1.

2.

3.

4.

5.

6.

6-13 What has been the ancestral background of all the empires during the first sixty-nine weeks (483 years) of Daniel's seventy week prophecy? (p. 105)

THE MYSTERIOUS SEVENTH BEAST EMPIRE

6-14 According to Revelation 17:10, a seventh beast empire will exist for a little while although it is not mentioned in Nebuchadnezzar's dream. Using the chart on page 107, why is this seventh empire not mentioned by Daniel? (pp. 105-107)

6-15 According to Daniel 9:26a, what caused the gap between the sixty-ninth and seventieth weeks? (p. 108)

6-16 Why is this mysterious seventh beast empire mentioned only in Revelation 17:10? (pp. 108-109)

6-17 With this in mind, is the seventh beast empire introduced in the Bible before or after the start of the Great Diaspora that began in A.D. 70?

6-18 What makes the seventh beast empire radically different from the first six beast empires? (p. 109)

6-19 What are the six essential characteristics of the seventh beast empire. (p. 109)

    1.

    2.

    3.

    4.

    5.

    6.

6-20 Who was this seventh beast empire? (p. 109)

6-21 If the Third Reich was Nazi Germany, who was the Second Reich?
(p. 491 endnote 11)

6-22 And who was the First Reich? (p. 491 endnote 11)

6-23 What other historical reasons indicate that Nazi Germany was the perfect candidate for being the seventh beast empire? (pp. 109-110)

A PREVIEW OF THE EIGHTH BEAST EMPIRE

6-24 As we preview the eighth beast empire, what will be its characteristics? (p. 110)

Personal Notes & Quotes:

CHAPTER
SEVEN

THE EIGHTH AND FINAL BEAST EMPIRE

F **CHAPTER FOCUS:**

The eighth beast empire will be the last beast empire of Satan, the beast empire that Satan will use in the last days in his attempt to destroy Israel and those who profess the name of Christ. In this chapter you will learn the ancestry of the ten nations that will make up this final beast empire, and in particular, the ancestry of the three nations that Antichrist will directly rule himself — his power-base nations that he will use to drive the other seven.

R **Read chapter 7 of *The Sign* before answering the following questions.**

7-1 What is your explanation of the following quote: "History should never determine prophetic interpretation, but rather prophetic truth should always be the basis for understanding the events of history?" (p. 113)

....

....

....

WHAT CAN WE KNOW?

7-2 After reading and carefully examining Daniel 2:41-43; 7:7-8, 19,20, 23-25 and Revelation 13:1, 3, 7-8, what is the significance of the relationship of the final beast empire with the Roman Empire? (pp. 115-116)

....

....

....

THE TABLE OF NATIONS

7-3 What does the Table of Nations recorded in Genesis 10 do? (p. 114)

7-4 As a general rule of thumb, what is an easy way to remember the ancestry of Noah's three sons, at least as they pertain to the beast empires of Satan? (p. 116)

THE HISTORICAL MOVEMENT OF THE NATIONS

7-5 Some three hundred years after the flood, how did Shem, Ham and Japheth, as well as their descendants, disobey God (see Genesis 9:1; 11:4)? (p. 117)

7-6 According to Genesis 11:9, how did God respond to this rebellion? (pp. 117-118)

7-7 Which of the sons of Japheth are normally considered to be the nomadic tribes, initially exploring the sections of the world north of Babel (or Babylon)? (p. 118)

7-8 What direction did the families of Magog, Meshech and Tubal initially go, and, according to Acts 17:26, why? (p. 118)

7-9 As we look at the ten nations that will comprise the eighth beast empire, what is the key issue to remember in our attempt to accurately identify them? (p. 118)

Iron Mixed With Clay

7-10 What is the significance of the "mixture of iron and clay" that God's Word gives in describing the feet (the final beast empire) of Nebuchadnezzar's statue? (p. 119)

Tracing the Roman Ancestry

7-11 In ancient times, were the Romans the initial inhabitants of the land known today as Italy? (pp. 119-120)

7-12 In our study of the history of Rome then, it is probable that the founders of Rome were the descendants of which of the sons of Japheth? (p. 121)

7-13 Why is it critical for the serious prophecy student, in the author's opinion, to accurately identify the ancestry of the three nations that will make up the power-base of the final beast empire? (p. 123)

DEFENSE FOR EZEKIEL 38-39

> ***Note:*** To properly identify the ancestry of the peoples that will drive the final beast empire of Satan, Ezekiel chapters 38-39 are critical. However, many scholars would have you believe that this critical passage either does not deal with prophetic end times or else, if dealing with the last days, is not speaking of Antichrist and his final beast empire. This author will not accept that thinking. Ezekiel's perspective may have differed, as well as his terminology — like so many other biblical writers on similar topics — but when looked at carefully, there is no doubt in this writer's mind that Ezekiel is referring directly to Antichrist and his armies, in relationship to the seventieth week of Daniel, a prophecy which, by the way, was not yet written when Ezekiel wrote this critical passage. For that reason, let us consider the reasons why this critical passage must be viewed from the perspective of Antichrist and the seventieth week of Daniel.

7-14 There are seven very good reasons why Ezekiel 38,39 must occur in association with the events of the seventieth week of Daniel. Give the <u>first reason</u>. (pp. 472-473 endnote 6)

....

7-15 Give the <u>second reason</u>. (pp. 472-473 endnote 6)

....

....

7-16 Give the <u>third reason</u>. (pp. 472-473 endnote 6)

....

....

7-17 Give the <u>fourth reason</u>. (pp. 472-473 endnote 6)

1. ....

2. ....

....

3. ....

7-18 Give the <u>fifth</u> and perhaps one of the strongest arguments. (pp. 472-473 endnote 6)

7-19 Give the <u>sixth</u> compelling reason. (pp. 472-473 endnote 6)

7-20 Give the <u>seventh</u> and final reason the author gives to establish his premise that Ezekiel 38-39 must refer to exactly the same events as described in the book of Revelation. (pp. 472-473 endnote 6)

THE THREE POWER-BASE NATIONS IDENTIFIED

7-21 Ezekiel 38:2,3 gives us our first clue on who the three power-base nations will be that Antichrist uses in the last days. Identify these three ancestral lines of Noah from the table of nations given in Genesis 10. (p. 123)

7-22 Discuss the possibilities surrounding "Rosh," as it pertains to the table of nations. (pp. 125, 474 endnote 8)

7-23 What is the most accurate meaning of the Hebrew word "Rosh"? (p. 123)

7-24 If "Rosh" then refers to leadership (chief prince), what will be the ancestry of the three nations over which Gog will rule, and from which of these three will Gog come? (p. 124)

7-25 According to Jewish Rabbinical writings, what is the identity of the ancestry of Magog? (pp. 124, 474 endnotes 9-10)

7-26 What is the identity of Meshech and Tubal? (pp. 125-126, 474-475 endnote 14)

7-27 With these considerations in mind, what is the logical conclusion regarding the ancestry of the founders of the Roman Empire? (p. 127)

7-28 Why was the breakup of the Soviet Union so important for the alignment of the nations in the last days? (p. 126)

7-29 What will characterize the ancestry of all three of the power-base nations? (p. 128)

THREE SECONDARY NATIONS IDENTIFIED BY DANIEL

7-30 According to Daniel 2:44, when the God of heaven destroys the final beast empire of Satan, who else does He destroy at the same time? (p. 129)

7-31 Logically speaking then, if God destroys "all these kingdoms" at the same time the final beast empire of Satan is destroyed, would it be fair to assume that ancestry from these previous kingdoms, therefore, must also be a part of the final beast empire? (p. 129 — See, in addition, author's comments on Dan. 7:11,12, p. 130)

7-32 Which three ancestral lines (of the seven secondary nations) are identified in Daniel 2:31-35? (pp. 129-131)

7-33 Where are the descendants of the ancient Babylonian Empire located today? (p. 129)

7-34 Where are the descendants of the ancient Medo-Persian Empire located today? (p. 131)

7-35 Where are the descendants of the ancient Greek Empire located today? (p. 131)

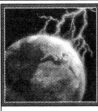

7-36 Comparing Scripture with Scripture, how does Revelation 13:1,2, when compared with Daniel 7:4-7, back up the premise that the gold, silver and iron kingdoms will be included in the final beast empire of iron and clay? (p. 130)

FOUR SECONDARY NATIONS IDENTIFIED BY EZEKIEL

7-37 According to Ezekiel 38:5,6, what is the ancestry of the remaining four nations that comprise the final beast empire of Satan? (p. 131)

7-38 What is the biblical ancestry of Ethiopia, and where are they located today? (p. 131)

7-39 What is the biblical ancestry of Put, and where are they located today? (p. 131)

7-40 What is the biblical ancestry of Gomer, and where are they located today? (pp. 131-132)

7-41 What is the biblical ancestry of Togarmah, and where are they located today? (p. 132)

SIGNIFICANCE OF THE TEN NATIONS

7-42 In relationship to the ancestry of the ten nations, what significant fact immediately becomes apparent? (p. 132)

7-43 Which two of the seven previous beast empires will not be included in the final beast empire, and why? (p. 133)

....

....

....

7-44 As you study the map on page 135, what is the significance of Joel 3:11-12 and Zechariah 12:6? (pp. 134-135)

....

....

....

Personal Notes & Quotes:

CHAPTER EIGHT

ANTICHRIST AND HIS FORESHADOW

F **CHAPTER FOCUS:**

Antichrist will be the leader of the final beast empire, and in this chapter you will learn what kind of a leader he will be. God has given us a foreshadow of Antichrist in the person and rule of Antiochus Epiphanes, who conquered and ravaged Israel and the Temple during the second century, B.C. The following questions are designed to show you the incredible similarities of these two ungodly leaders, and what can expected by those going into the seventieth week of Daniel.

R **Read chapter 8 of *The Sign* before answering the following questions.**

8-1 Daniel 7:8-27 specifically has the last days in view, with Antichrist specifically in view in verse 8. To what is Antichrist likened? (p. 139)

_____

8-2 Likewise, Daniel 8:9-26 specifically has the reign of Antiochus Epiphanes in view. To what is Antiochus specifically likened in verse 9? (p. 139)

_____

8-3 Who is this former despot who parallels Antichrist? (p. 138)

_____

SEVEN SIGNIFICANT PARALLELS

8-4 Seven similarities or parallels between Antiochus Epiphanies and Antichrist are given in order that we may better understand how Antichrist will operate in the last days. Give the <u>first similarity</u>. (p. 143)

_____

8-5 Give the <u>second similarity</u>. (pp. 143-144)

8-6 Give the <u>third similarity</u>. (p. 144)

8-7 Give the <u>fourth similarity</u>. (p. 144)

8-8 Give the <u>fifth similarity</u>. (p. 144)

8-9 Give the <u>sixth similarity</u>. (p. 144)

8-10 Give the <u>seventh and final similarity</u> between Antiochus and Antichrist. (p. 144)

8-11 How can awareness of these similarities help us as we live in the last days just prior to end time events? (p. 143)

THE LAST TRUMPET OF GOD

> *Note:* There has been considerable confusion concerning the "trumpet of God" that sounds at the rapture of the true church at the second coming of Christ. Some relate it to the seventh trumpet judgment, blown by an angel of God in the book of Revelation. Others try to relate it to some other specific blowing of a trumpet found elsewhere in Scripture. In every case where this comparison is made to justify when the Rapture will occur, the blowing referred to is always by an angel of God — representing God — and thus used to prove the time sequence being argued. This author disagrees. He believes that "trumpet of God" is specifically that, the "trumpet of God," and when compared to its only other use in the Word of God, gives the student of biblical prophecy greater understanding of why it is specifically referred to in the last days.

8-12 Because of the controversy surrounding the "last trumpet" (1 Corinthians 15:52) "of God" (1 Thessalonians 4:16), we need to look carefully at exactly what Scripture is really teaching. To begin with, how many times do the Scriptures refer directly to God, not an angel, blowing a trumpet? (p. 144)

THE RISE OF ANTICHRIST

8-13 What is the interesting parallel found in the two instances where God is directly shown blowing the trumpet? (pp. 144, 475 endnote 2)

8-14 What have we learned about Antichrist's strategy in this chapter? (p. 145)

Personal Notes & Quotes:

CHAPTER NINE

THE STAGE IS SET

F **CHAPTER FOCUS:**

Where are we in God's timetable today? This chapter shows you how our sovereign God will set the stage for the final events on this earth. You will look at the condition of the world we live in today, and see how it fulfills prophecy concerning the condition of the world going into the seventieth week of Daniel.

You will learn the importance of understanding near/far prophecy and why, as we view today's conditions, believers should be prepared for end times as never before.

R **Read chapter 9 of *The Sign* before answering the following questions.**

PRIOR CONDITIONS

9-1 What two crucial events have already occurred today, setting the stage for end time events? (p. 147)

THE GENERAL DECAY IN CULTURE

9-2 How does today's culture compare to what the Bible says in 2 Timothy 3:1-5? (p. 148)

9-3 What is the first condition that must exist in the world before the seventieth week can commence? (p. 148)

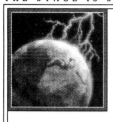

9-4 Under the condition of "The General Decay in Culture" how does the music of our day relate to the general decay in culture evidenced in the last days? (p. 149)

9-5 How do current films relate to the general decay of our culture today? (p. 150)

9-6 How does contemporary art relate to the general decay of our culture? (pp. 150-151)

THE GENERAL CLIMATE OF THOUGHT

9-7 After reading 2 Timothy 4:3-4 and 1 Timothy 4:1,7, what is the second prior condition necessary before the seventieth week of Daniel can commence? (pp. 151-152)

9-8 How does the New Age Movement qualify under the second prior condition? (pp. 152-155)

9-9 According to 2 Peter 3:4,5, what will be the world's dominant scientific system of thought as it enters the seventieth week of Daniel? (p. 158)

9-10 How does 2 Peter 3:3-7 perfectly describe what is known today as scientific uniformitarianism? (p. 155)

9-11 How does scientific uniformitarianism affect us today? (pp. 155-156)

9-12 According to Romans 1:18-20, in what one area does God hold all mankind accountable, whether or not they have ever heard the gospel of Jesus Christ? (p. 156)

9-13 What major flaw does scientific uniformitarianism have? (p. 156)

THE GENERAL CONDITION OF THE CHURCH

9-14 After reading 2 Timothy 4:3,4 and 2 Peter 2:1-3, 13-15, what is the third prior condition given that will be in existence when the seventieth week begins? (pp. 158-159)

9-15 Why should this be a major concern to every true Christian entering into the last days? (p. 159, see in particular Matt. 24:9-12)

9-16 What are unbiblical prophetic views doing to the church today? (p. 159)

9-17 Using biblical common sense and comparing carefully 1 Peter 1:6,7 with 1 John 2:28, why does the moral decay of the church in the last days, demand that the church go through the great tribulation of Antichrist?

9-18 Explain near/far prophetic truth as related to the seven churches of Revelation, chapters 2-3. (p. 161)

9-19 How do we know that the seven churches of Revelation, chapters 2-3, have end-time significance? (p. 161)

9-20 What does a study of chapters 2-3 of Revelation, reveal as to the condition of the church just prior to the second coming of Christ? (p. 162)

9-21 What is the significance of the phrase "everyone who has an ear, let him hear"? (pp. 162-163)

9 CHAPTER NINE

9-22 According to 1 Peter 4:12, 17,18, why does the church have to go through the "fiery testing"? (p. 163)

9-23 How does this passage square with 1 Peter 1:5-7?

9-24 What will the compromising church (both spiritually alive and dead Christians) experience as they face the seventieth week? (p. 164)

9-25 What will the spiritually dead church (unsaved church goers) experience as they face the seventieth week? (p. 164)

9-26 What will the faithful church (true Christians) experience as they face the seventieth week? (p. 164)

9-27 What does the Lord mean when He exhorts believers in Revelation 2:7, 11, 17, 26; 3:5, 12, 21, to be "overcomers?" (p. 164)

9-28 According to 1 John 5:4,5, who is the true overcomer? (p. 164)

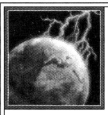

THE RETURN OF UNBELIEVING JEWS TO ISRAEL

9-29 According to Deuteronomy 30:3,6 and Ezekiel 36:24-25, will Israel return to her land in belief or unbelief? (p. 168)

9-30 According to Daniel 9:24, when does "everlasting righteousness" occur for the nation of Israel in relation to the seventieth week, and how does this substantiate the nation's return to Israel in unbelief? (pp. 166-167)

9-31 Why is it important that prophecy be literally fulfilled, especially as it pertains to the nation of Israel? (pp. 168-169)

THE CONTROL OF JERUSALEM BY ISRAEL

9-32 In the same way that the Diaspora "triggered" the interlude between the sixty-ninth and seventieth weeks, what two events will "trigger" the initiation of the seventieth week of Daniel, that specific seven year period when the final conflict between God and Satan will be played out on earth? (p. 170)

9-33 According to Daniel 9:24, why is it important that Israel control Jerusalem before the seventieth week begins? (p. 170)

9-34 Does there need to be a temple built on Mount Zion in Jerusalem before the seventieth week can commence? Why or why not? (pp. 171, 476-477 endnote 21)

THE THREE-NATION POWER BASE

9-35 What one event remains before the seventieth week can commence and why is it so important? (pp. 172-175, 477-478 endnote 23)

9-36 In regards to this three nation power-base, we should pay close attention to the events that occur in what particular area of the world? (p. 173)

Personal Notes & Quotes:

CHAPTER
TEN

COUNTDOWN TO THE END OF THE AGE

F **CHAPTER FOCUS:**

   This is a very important chapter as you look at the signing of the covenant between Antichrist and Israel which initiates the seventieth week, and you begin to understand the events that occur during the first 3 1/2 years and the relevance of these events to the church that enters into the last days. You will begin to understand the price for compromise in the church in general, and come to understand why clearly the six seal events of the seventieth week described in Revelation 6, cannot be the wrath of God, but rather the wrath of Satan that God permits for the purification and refinement of the compromising church going into the seventieth week. Finally, you will examine some of the characteristics of the Babylonian Harlot.

R **Read chapter 10 of *The Sign* before answering the following questions. Note however, that if the first edition of *The Sign* is being used, the author has made some significant changes to the material presented in this chapter. If, however, the expanded edition is being used, the material tracks perfectly with the book.**

A COVENANT WITH DEATH

10-1   According to Daniel 9:27, what event initiates the seventieth week of Daniel, and what does this event initiate within the nation herself? (p. 178)

_____

_____

10-2   What does 2 Thessalonians 2:3 — in parallel with Hosea 14:4 — call this ultimate unfaithfulness of Israel? (p. 178)

_____

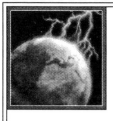

10-3 What does Isaiah 28:15, 18 call this specific covenant with Antichrist? (p. 178)

10-4 As you study the near fulfillment of this prophecy — fulfilled in the days of Antiochus Epiphanes (Daniel 11:23, 30, 32) — how does the near-term fulfillment parallel the far-term fulfillment of this prophecy in the days of Antichrist? (p. 179)

10-5 Will Christians be aware of the signing of the covenant between Israel and Antichrist? (p. 180)

A FALSE SECURITY

10-6 Looking at Amos 9:10 and Ezekiel 38:11, what will best characterize the milieu in the land of Israel during the first three and one-half years of the seventieth week? (pp. 180-181)

THE JEWISH WITNESSES

10-7 Reading Matthew 10:16, 23, will the entire nation of Israel apostatize to the Antichrist when the covenant is made (while he is still incognito, before he reveals his true identity), or will only a portion of the nation follow this ungodly leader? (pp. 181, 478-479 endnote 2)

THE LARGE SCROLL OF REVELATION

10-8 According to Revelation 5:1, John saw how many seals on the large scroll in God's right hand? (p. 181)

10-9 If John could see all seven seals on the large scroll, would that indicate that the seals were on the outside of the scroll, or one on the outside and the other six all on the inside? (p. 181)

10-10 What must happen to the seven seals on the outside of the scroll before the scroll can be opened? (p. 181)

10-11 According to Revelation 5:5, who do the elders indicate is worthy to open the seals of the large scroll? (p. 181)

10-12 According to Revelation 5:6, 9, who does the "Lion" from the tribe of Judah refer to? (p. 182)

10-13 When referring to Christ as the "Lion" rather than the "Lamb," to what does this refer? (p. 182)

10-14 What do the seven seals on the outside of the scroll represent? In other words, why seven seals? Why not only one, instead? (p. 182)

10-15 When seals are found on ancient scrolls, where are they always located? (p. 182)

10-16 In relationship to the large scroll of Revelation, why is this so significant? (p. 182)

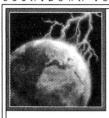

10-17   According to Acts 17:31, why is Christ "the Lamb" worthy to open the scroll as "the Lion"? (p. 182)

10-18   If only the "Lion of Judah" — Christ as Judge — can open the large scroll of the book of Revelation, what would be a fair assumption as to the contents of the scroll, knowing in advance the basic thrust of Revelation?

JUDGMENT BEGINS WITH THE HOUSEHOLD OF GOD

10-19   If the large scroll represents God's judgment of the kingdom of darkness according to 1 Peter 4:17, 18 what must occur first? (p. 183)

10-20   Comparing Revelation, chapters 2-3 (which describes the general condition of the church going into the last days) with 2 Timothy 3:1-5, what will be the church's spiritual condition in the last days?

10-21   According to 1 Peter 1:7 and 1 John 2:28, what will be the response of every professing Christian when Christ returns?

10-22   In other words, if "judgment begins with the household of faith," the church will be put to the test just prior to Christ's judgment of the world. How is this assumption confirmed by 1 Peter 4:12-13 and further confirmed by Revelation 2:22-23?

10-23 How is this "fiery ordeal" that comes upon the church for "your testing" (1 Peter 4:12), described in Revelation 3:10?

THE SERAPHIM

10-24 According to Isaiah 6:2, where do the Seraphim reside, and what is distinctively different about them? (p. 183)

10-25 According to Isaiah 6:3-7, what two specific things are the Seraphim doing around the throne of God? (p. 183)

10-26 If, according to 1 Peter 4:17, "judgment begins with the household of faith" before God judges the kingdom of darkness, and having gained a better understanding concerning the roll of the Seraphim from our text in Isaiah 6, who would we expect to see in heaven bringing about the purification of the church before they are raptured into the actual presence of God?

10-27 According to Revelation 4:6-8, how are the "four living creatures" described, where are they, and what are they saying? (p. 183)

10-28 Therefore, comparing Scripture (Rev. 4:6-8) with Scripture (Isa. 6:2-3), the four living creatures can only be whom?

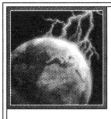

10-29 According to Revelation 6:1, 3, 5, 7, these four living creatures are directly associ
ated with the first four seals. Therefore, keeping in mind 1 Peter 1: 6,7 and
4:16,17, what might we assume to be God's purpose in permitting the events associated with the first four seals? (p. 184)

THE BEGINNING OF "BIRTH-PANGS"

> *Note:* With the foregoing in mind, the fact that the judgment begins with the household of faith (the process of purifying a compromising church before it comes into the presence of God); the fact that the judgment of the household of faith is followed by the judgment of God upon the kingdom of darkness (1 Peter 4:17-18); and the fact that the four living creatures that surround the throne of God are the Seraphim of God that protect God's holiness, we are now ready to proceed with the opening of the seven seals of the large scroll. Remember, the seals are the conditions that must be met before the scroll, describing God's judgment of the wicked, can be opened by Christ, the Lion, the Judge.

10-30 As we learned in the first chapter of this book, what passage of Scripture — other than the book of
Revelation — gives us the best understanding of the book of Revelation? (p. 184)

10-31 Why does the Olivet Discourse give us such a clear understanding of the book of Revelation?
(p. 184)

> *Note:* However, before we continue on with the opening of the individual seals, we must understand clearly why the four horsemen of Revelation 6 – that represent the first four seals – while permitted by God for the purification of the household of faith, definitely cannot be the wrath of God – the day of the Lord – as many churches today teach in an attempt to keep the church out of the seventieth week of Daniel.

THE SEVENTIETH WEEK NOT THE DAY OF THE LORD

10-32 The author gives eight reasons why the first five seals of Revelation 6 cannot be considered the wrath of God. Give the <u>first reason</u>. (p. 186)

10-33 Give the <u>second reason</u>. (p. 186)

10-34 Where in Revelation is the first mention of God's wrath, and to what event is it linked that makes this first mention so significant? (p. 186)

10-35 Give the <u>third reason</u> why the first five seals cannot be the wrath of God. (p. 186)

10-36 If, as some say, the first seal will be God's wrath, why according to Matthew 12:25,26, is this an unthinkable position? (p. 186)

10-37 Give the <u>fourth reason</u>. (p. 187)

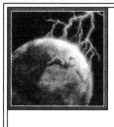

10-38 According to Romans 5:9 and 1 Thessalonians 5:8,9, why does the fifth seal cause a problem in designating all the seals as God's wrath? (p. 187)

10-39 Give the <u>fifth reason</u>. (p. 187)

10-40 If according to Isaiah 2:17 "the Lord alone shall be exalted in that day [of the Lord]," why is it a contradiction for the entire seventieth week to be the day of the Lord? (p. 187)

10-41 Give the <u>sixth reason</u>. (pp. 187-188)

10-42 According to the Olivet Discourse (Matthew 24:6, 9, 13), what does Christ specifically tell His disciples must happen before the end of the age (the day of the Lord) can begin? (p. 188)

10-43 Give the <u>seventh reason</u> why the first five seals cannot be God's wrath. (p. 188)

10-44 What does the "these things" refer to in Matthew 24:33 and why does a proper understanding of what "these things" are make it impossible to equate the entire seventieth week with the wrath of God? (p. 188)

Note: Some men, arguing that the seal events are the wrath of God, use Ezekiel 14:21 as a proof text for their argument. Because at face value there seems to be some merit to their argument, this author feels that it is important for us to understand why their argument cannot hold water, not only because all of the other teachings of Scripture concerning the timing of God's wrath – including Revelation 12:12 – but because a careful analysis of Ezekiel 14:21, on its own account, cannot support their argument.

EZEKIEL 14:21 DEFENSE

10-45 If the "four severe judgments" mentioned in this text are referring to the seal events described in Revelation 6, what is obviously missing? (pp. 479-481 endnote 3)

10-46 Which specific Hebrew word is translated "wrath" in Ezekiel 14:21, and what is this word's broader meaning? (p. 480 endnote 3)

10-47 What is the only Hebrew word translated "wrath" when describing God's day-of-the-Lord wrath, and what is its broader meaning? (p. 480 endnote 3)

10-48 What is always the context of the Hebrew word "Ebrah"? (p. 480 endnote 3)

10-49   Against whom is God's day-of-the-Lord wrath (Ebrah) primarily directed? (p. 480 endnote 3)

10-50   To whom is the wrath in Ezekiel 14:21 directed? (p. 480 endnote 3)

10-51   Therefore, based upon the foregoing, what can we conclude about the wrath of God and the first 6 seal events outlined in Revelation 6?

10-52   In summary of this argument concerning whose wrath is represented during the seventieth week of Daniel, especially during the great tribulation of Antichrist, who does Revelation 12:12 attribute this wrath to?

THE BEGINNING OF BIRTH PANGS

Note: We now return to our premise that "judgment begins with the household of faith" before God's wrath is poured out upon those who do not obey the gospel of God (1 Peter 4:17-18). As we begin now to look specifically at the seals that have to be opened by Christ before the scroll can be opened and the wrath of God begins, remember that it is the Seraphim that release the events associated with the first four seals. These events are permitted by God for the purification and refinement of the compromising church that goes into the last days, not that unlike the continual purification and refinement of Israel we see recorded in the Old Testament. Therefore, the Seraphim are not the source of the events, they simply oversee these events permitted by God. Nothing can happen, including Satan's direct access to mankind at the midpoint of the seventieth week, without God's permission. Therefore, the events that are directly associated with the seven seals of Revelation are those events that must occur before God will give Christ, the Lion, the right to open the scroll and begin the wrath of God upon the earth, an event known in Scripture as the Day of the Lord.

In order to assist our understanding of what occurs in Revelation we must refer to the Olivet Discourse of Christ. Only when the two accounts are put together, will the student of prophecy begin to put the pieces of the prophetic puzzle together accurately.

The first three seal events described in the book of Revelation are referred to by Christ as "the beginning of birth pangs" in the Olivet Discourse as recorded in Matthew 24.

THE FIRST THREE SEALS

10-53 According to Matthew 24:5 and Luke 21:8, when compared to Revelation 6:1-2, what does the first seal represent, and how can we be sure? (p. 189)

_____

_____

10-54 Why will the first seal have direct significance for true Christians? (p. 189)

_____

_____

10-55 What will be the condition of the church in general that will go into the seventieth week, and why? (pp. 189-190)

_____

_____

10-56 What is the major problem in the great majority of the "professing" churches going into the seventieth week? (p. 190)

_____

_____

10-57 What is a serious teaching error affecting a great percentage of the "professing" churches going into the last days? (p. 190)

_____

_____

10-58 What is the specific teaching error concerning end times in the majority of evangelical churches today? (p. 190)

_____

_____

10-59 How will the faithful church, which has been carefully and accurately taught the Word of God, face the seventieth week? (p. 191)

10-60 According to Matthew 24:6,7 and Revelation 6:3,4, what will occur when the second seal is opened? (p. 193)

10-61 What will Antichrist be doing during the second seal? (p. 193)

10-62 According to Revelation 17:12,13 who else will give allegiance to Antichrist during the first half of the seventieth week, helping in the consolidation of the eight beast empire? (p. 194)

10-63 According to Matthew 24:7 and Revelation 6:5,6, what seems to be the emphasis of the third seal, when it is opened? (p. 196)

10-64 How does the author believe that Antichrist will use this time of worldwide famine to his own advantage? (p. 196)

10-65 What does Matthew 24:8 call the first three seals of Revelation? (p. 196)

10-66 Chronologically, where does the completion of the third seal bring us in the sequence of events during the seventieth week? (p. 196)

THE BABYLONIAN HARLOT

> ***Note:*** Before we conclude this chapter, we must look at one other significant event that was referred to as occurring during the first half of the seventieth week. Antichrist is building his own empire in preparation for the events that will occur during the second half of the seventieth week. It is here, in the author's opinion, that the Babylonian Harlot is introduced, as well as the part she plays in the last days.

10-67 According to Daniel 11:39, Antichrist will be assisted in building his empire during the first half of the seventieth week with the help of a "foreign god." Who is the likely candidate to become this "foreign god," and why? (p. 194, 483-486 endnote 7)

10-68 Who is the Babylonian Harlot? (pp. 194, 483-486 endnote 7)

10-69 There are seven dominant characteristics of the Babylonian Harlot found in Revelation 17:1-7, 9, 15, 18. Give the <u>first characteristic</u>. (pp. 483-484 endnote 7)

10-70 Give the <u>second characteristic</u> of the Babylonian Harlot. (p. 484 endnote 7)

10-71 Give the <u>third characteristic</u>. (p. 484 endnote 7)

10-72 Give the <u>fourth characteristic</u>. (p. 484 endnote 7)

10-73 Give the <u>fifth characteristic</u>. (p. 484 endnote 7)

10-74 Give the <u>sixth characteristic</u>. (p. 484 endnote 7)

10-75 Give the <u>seventh characteristic</u> of the Babylonian Harlot. (pp. 484-485 endnote 7)

CHAPTER
ELEVEN

ANTICHRIST REVEALED

F **CHAPTER FOCUS:**

In this chapter you will see that Antichrist does not reveal his true identity until the mid-point of the seventieth week and what the response of people will be when they see and understand who this man really is. You will learn about an uncompromising remnant of unbelieving Israel, "the woman," and how and where she flees for protection. You will also look at and identify the restrainer who has restrained Satan's direct attack upon Israel — as well as the saints of God — up unto this point in the history of mankind. You will also see what facts Scripture gives concerning the identity of Antichrist and the logical conclusion the author comes to based upon this information.

R **Read chapter 11 of *The Sign* before answering the following questions.**

THE JERUSALEM CAMPAIGN

11-1 What will be the event that will initiate the violation of the covenant between Antichrist and Israel? (p. 200)

11-2 What Old Testament prophecies depict Antichrist's invasion of Jerusalem and why should the Jews living there be concerned? (p. 201)

11-3 How does Daniel 12:1 describe this particular time that comes as a result of Antichrist's breaking of the covenant?

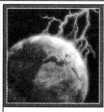

11-4 How does Isaiah 28:19 (NAS) describe Israel's reaction when they begin to "understand what it means"?

11-5 According to Matthew 24:15 and 2 Thessalonians 2:4, what event marks the beginning of the second half of the seventieth week? That event that will initiate the great tribulation by Antichrist. (p. 200)

11-6 Where does Antichrist's extreme hatred for Jews come from? (p. 202)

"THE WOMAN" WHO FLEES

11-7 How will some Jews respond? (pp. 203-204)

11-8 According to Daniel 11:41, does Antichrist control Edom at the time this small remnant of Jews flee to the Edomite wilderness? (p. 204)

11-9 According to Obadiah 12-15, what warning does God give to Edom concerning those Jews who flee to the Edomite wilderness in "the day of their [Israel's] disaster"? (p. 204)

11-10 If God warns Edom that their mistreatment of the Jewish wilderness remnant during "the day of their [Israel's] disaster," will result in God's wrath — the day of the Lord — against Edom, does that mean that the day of the Lord follows or precedes the great tribulation (the day of their [Israel's] disaster) against Israel?

11-11 What Jewish group fits the description of "the woman" that flees into the wilderness and why? (pp. 205, 486-487 endnote 1)

SATAN THROWN DOWN TO EARTH

11-12 According to Revelation 12:7-10, what happens to Satan at the mid-point of the seventieth week? (p. 205)

11-13 What is the first thing Satan will attempt to prevent when he finds himself no longer able to accuse the elect before the throne of God, no more having access to heaven? (p. 206)

11-14 In addition, who else becomes a target of Satan when he is thrown down to earth? (p. 206)

SATAN EMPOWERS ANTICHRIST

11-15 According to Revelation 13:4, Satan gives his authority to whom, in order to accomplish his evil purposes against God, and what is the response of the world? (pp. 206-207)

11-16 Again, referring to a passage we have looked at several times already in our study together, according to Revelation 12:12, whose wrath is being executed upon earth during the persecution of Antichrist?

MICHAEL (THE RESTRAINER) REMOVED

11-17 According to Daniel 12:1, what "protection" for God's "chosen" (in particular, Israel, and more probably, the church as well) will be removed at this precise time, permitting Antichrist to begin his unrelentful attack upon Israel?

11-18 Define and explain the Hebrew word *'amad* as used in Daniel 12:1. (pp. 88-89 endnote 4)

11-19 Compare the use of the same word in Joshua 10:13 (NAS). (pp. 88-89 endnote 4)

11-20 What is Michael, the protector of Israel, called in 2 Thessalonians 2:6,7? (p. 208)

11-21 Where in Scripture is Michael called the restrainer? (pp. 207, 489 endnote 4)

11-22 Is the Holy Spirit or the church ever called the restrainer in Scripture?

11-23 According to Revelation 12:12,13, 17, when Michael "stands still" or "stops" his activity as Restrainer, what happens?

THE IDENTIFICATION OF ANTICHRIST

11-24 According to Revelation 13:4, why will the world worship Antichrist? (p. 210)

11-25 What startling fact is given concerning the identity of Antichrist in Revelation 13:3? (p. 209)

DESCRIPTIONS OF ANTICHRIST

11-26 Look up the following verses and give the ten names or titles attributed to Antichrist: 1 John 2:18; Revelation 13:4; 2 Thessalonians 2:3; Ezekiel 38:2; Daniel 7:8; 11:36; Isaiah 16:4; Habakkuk 3:13; and Matthew 24:15. (p. 210)

1.

2.

3.

4.

5.

6.

7.

8.

9.

10.

11-27 Accepting Matthew 24:15; Daniel 11:36; 2 Thessalonians 2:3,4 and Ezekiel 38:2 at face value, is Antichrist an individual or a nation? (p. 210)

11-28 How do we determine if the term "beast" is an individual or a nation? (p. 211)

11-29 Study Revelation 17:10,11 and list the nations of the five kings that had already fallen at the time the book of Revelation was written. (p. 211)

11-30 Who was the one king and nation that "now is" from John's perspective at the time Revelation was written? (p. 211)

11-31 Who is the king and nation that was still to come for a little while? (p. 211)

11-32 According to Revelation 17:11, where does the eighth king who rules over the eighth and final beast empire of Satan, come from? (pp. 211-212)

11-33 Comparing Revelation 13:3, 12 with Revelation 11:7, Antichrist, then, will be a previous beast empire leader who is what? and comes from where? to rule over the final beast empire of the last days.

NINE STARTLING FACTS

11-34 There are nine startling facts about the true identity of Antichrist given in Scripture. According to Daniel 11:36 and 2 Thessalonians, what is the first fact? (p. 212)

11-35 Referring to Ezekiel 38:4, 8, 9 and Daniel 11:38, what is a second fact we can know about the identity of Antichrist? (p. 213)

11-36 Referring to Revelation 13:12 and 2 Thessalonians 2:9, what is a third fact? (p. 213)

11-37 Looking Revelation 17:11, what will be a fourth fact? (p. 213)

11-38 Looking at Revelation 13:3, 14, what will be the fifth fact? (p. 213)

11-39 Looking at Revelation 13:3, 12 and 17:8, 11, what will be a sixth fact we can know concerning the identity of Antichrist? (p. 213)

11-40 According to Revelation 13:12; 17:8 and 2 Thessalonians 2:3, 4, what will be a seventh fact? (p. 213)

11-41 According to Ezekiel 38:2, what will be a eighth fact about Antichrist — the ancestral line of Antichrist? (p. 213)

11-42 And finally, according to Revelation 11:7, from whence does this man's soul come, when he is brought back to life to rule over the final beast empire of Satan? (p. 213)

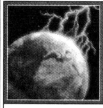

11-43 Why can we eliminate the leaders of the first five beast empires as possible candi dates for Antichrist? (pp. 213, 490 endnote 6)

THE SIXTH AND SEVENTH BEAST EMPIRES

11-44 What two beast empires, therefore, had leaders who had Magogite ancestry? (pp. 214-215)

11-45 If Antichrist was the leader of the ancient Roman Empire who will live again as the ruler of the final beast empire, which specific Roman leader must he be? (p. 214)

11-46 Who is the leader of the seventh beast empire, and why does he qualify to be Antichrist? (p. 215)

WHICH ONE?

11-47 What three crucial criteria fit both Nero and Hitler? (pp. 215-216)

1.

2.

3.

11-48 What two additional considerations (numbers 4 and 5) make the choice virtually indisputable? (p. 216)

1.

2.

11-49 Therefore, who, in the author's opinion, best fits the criteria for Antichrist? (p. 216)

11-50 As an aside, in the author's opinion, what would have had to happen for the seventh beast empire never to have become a reality, thereby making Nero the Antichrist? (p. 491 endnote 10)

11-51 After careful study of the section entitled "Who is this Man?," what are the obvious parallels between Hitler and the identity of Antichrist as revealed in God's Word? (pp. 217-221, 490-492 endnotes 9-11)

Personal Notes & Quotes:

CHAPTER
TWELVE

COUNTING THE COST

F **CHAPTER FOCUS:**

In this chapter you will not only see that the worship of Antichrist will indeed be worldwide, but also what it means to worship the image of the beast and how deadly it can be to those who do not. As there will also be considerable cost for either taking or refusing the mark of the beast, we must be prepared for the consequences before it happens. Counting the cost will be supernaturally assisted by three angelic messages that God will give the whole earth, forewarning the world in advance of the price of each individual's decision at this critical time in history.

R **Read chapter 12 of *The Sign* before answering the following questions.**

ANTICHRIST'S CONTROL OF EARTH

12-1 According to Revelation 13:3, how widespread will the worship of Antichrist be? (pp. 223-224)

....

....

12-2 How does Revelation 13:8 qualify the "whole world," and what latitude does this give unsaved Israel in general, that will not be saved until the completion of the seventieth week?

....

....

....

12-3 According to Revelation 13:14,15, what will the second beast — the enforcer for the first beast, Antichrist — "deceive" those who dwell on the earth into doing? (p. 226)

....

12-4 What is a better translation for the Greek term for "image"? (p. 226)

12-5 Does the Greek word translated "image" in this text, give us the right to interpret this passage with the view that each and every one will make his own individual statue to the beast, rather than just one worldwide, international monument to the beast? (pp. 492-493 endnote 1)

12-6 How does the context of this passage support this position? (p. 493 endnote 1)

12-7 According to Revelation 9:20, these idols will be made out of what materials?

12-8 In Revelation 13:15, what does the phrase "to give breath" mean? (p. 227, 493 endnote 2)

12-9 Again according to Revelation 9:20, what are the limitations that will be imposed upon these statues? (p. 227)

12-10 What significance do the limitations of these demonic statues have for believers? (p. 228)

12-11 From the passage in Matthew 8:28-32, what four truths can we observe about the nature and limitations of demons as they relate to the demon-indwelt statues or images of the end times? (pp. 228-229)

1.

2.

3.

4.

12-12 Comparing Revelation 13:15 with 12:9, how does it appear that these images to the beast will become demon-indwelt and empowered? (p. 230)

12-13 Why will it be of ultimate importance for Christians going into the seventieth week of Daniel to be aware of these demonic images? (p. 230)

THE TWO-FOLD TEST

12-14 According to Revelation 13:15-18, what will be the two-fold test carried out by Antichrist's enforcer, the second beast? (pp. 230-231)

1.

2.

12-15 As a result of the two-fold test, what critical dilemma will be facing every Christian? (p. 231)

12-16 In light of the second seal, the worldwide famines, and this author's contention that Antichrist will stockpile food supplies during the first half of the seventieth week, how will having the mark of Antichrist become an additional method of Antichrist's control of the world?

12-17 According to 1 Timothy 4:1, what will happen to some within the church in general? (p. 232)

12-18 According to Ezekiel 7:19-20, what will happen to some within the nation of Israel in general? (p. 232)

THE PERSEVERANCE OF THE SAINTS

12-19 In Revelation 3:10, God gives the faithful church the promise of protection during "the hour of testing" for what reason?

12-20 Define the word "perseverance" (Greek *hupomonē*). (pp. 233, 493 endnote 3)

THE THREE-ANGEL ANNOUNCEMENT

12-21 According to Revelation 14:6-13, God will give three messages to the world at the same time Antichrist demands the worship of the world. Who delivers these messages? (pp. 233-234)

12-22 What is the message of the first angel? (p. 234)

12-23 Why is the message of the first angel so important? (pp. 233-234)

12-24 Using 2 Corinthians 7:9-10, define and explain the "eternal gospel." (pp. 234-235)

12-25 How does the message of the first angel relate to Matthew 24:14? (p. 236)

12-26 What will be the message of the second angel, and what is the significance of it? (pp. 236-237)

12-27 What is significant about the message of the second angel? (p. 237)

12-28 According to Revelation 17:16, who will destroy the Babylonian Harlot? (p. 237)

12-29 Why do you believe Antichrist and his beast empire will need to destroy the Babylonian Harlot at this particular time, the midpoint of the seventieth week? (p. 237)

12-30 Distinguish between the "Babylonian Harlot" and "Babylon the Great." (pp. 237, 483 endnote 7, 516-517 endnote 3)

12-31 When will the Babylonian Harlot be destroyed? (p. 237)

12-32 When will Babylon the Great (city) be destroyed? (p. 516 endnote 3)

12-33 What is the message of the third angel, and why is it so important? (p. 238)

12-34 When the third angel's warning is given, is God's wrath past or future? (p. 238)

12-35 What does the third angel's announcement (Rev. 14:9-11) do to those who equate the entire seventieth week (beginning with the first seal) to the day of the Lord (God's wrath)? (p. 238)

The Two Witnesses

12-36 When will the "two witnesses" (Rev. 11:3-6) come onto the scene in reference to Daniel's seventieth week? (pp. 239, 494 endnote 6)

12-37 What will be the two major priorities in the ministry of the two witnesses? (p. 240)

1.

2.

12-38 According to Revelation 11:3, how long will the ministry of the two witnesses extend? (p. 239)

12-39 Who will these two witnesses likely be? (pp. 239, 494 endnote 6)

Personal Notes & Quotes:

CHAPTER
THIRTEEN

THE GREAT TRIBULATION BY ANTICHRIST

F **CHAPTER FOCUS:**

The Great Tribulation (the persecution of Antichrist) will be the focus of this chapter. You will look more carefully at those who will be the targets of Antichrist's persecution, the severity of the Great Tribulation, and the methods by which the persecution of Antichrist will be carried out. You will also be given more understanding as to why God permits the persecution to take place and finally, why the early church lived in expectation of the return of Christ.

R **Read chapter 13 of *The Sign* before answering the following questions.**

TRIBULATION WITH NO EQUAL

13-1 According to Matthew 24:21, what is the Great Tribulation? (p. 244)

....

....

13-2 Based upon what we have learned thus far in this study, when will the great tribulation of Antichrist occur?

....

....

13-3 According to Revelation 12:12 cf. 13:2, the great tribulation is the wrath of whom?

....

....

13-4 According to Revelation 12:13,14, 17, who will be Antichrist's main targets? (p. 245)

"THE WOMAN"

13-5 Who is "the woman" mentioned in Revelation 12:14? (pp. 245, 495 endnote 2)

13-6 According to Ezekiel 20:37, when does "the woman" who flees to the wilderness, come under the bond of the covenant (into saving relationship) with her true Messiah and King? (p. 495 endnote 3)

13-7 As the rest of Israel will not be saved until the "fullness of the Gentiles has come in" (see Rom. 11:25-26), which cannot occur until after the completion of the seventieth week of Daniel (see Dan. 9:24), what does Revelation 14:4 call this new remnant of Jewish believers? (p. 495 endnote 3)

13-8 In the same text (Rev. 14:4), how specifically does John identify these "first fruits [from the nation of Israel] to God and to the Lamb"? (p. 486 endnote 1; 495 endnote 3)

13-9 Now, refreshing your memory (see page 486 endnote 1, second point), to what does Revelation 14:4 refer when it says "they have kept themselves chaste" and how does that apply to "the woman"?

"THE REST OF HER OFFSPRING"

13-10 Who are the "rest of her offspring" mentioned in Revelation 12:17? (pp. 246-247, 495-496 endnote 4)

13-11 How do we know that the "rest of the offspring" of "the woman" does not refer only to men and women of Jewish ancestry? (pp. 495-496 endnote 4)

13-12 Therefore, based upon the previous question, why isn't the "rest of her offspring" Jewish believers who come to know Christ during the seventieth week in addition to the 144,000 first fruits? (p. 495 endnote 3)

13-13 According to Galatians 3:29, how can we equate the "rest of her offspring" with both Jewish and Gentile Christians?

THE FOURTH SEAL: DEATH AND HADES

Note: A short review is in order here. After Satan has been thrown down to earth with his angels, cleansing the heavenlies as it were, and the restrainer (the angelic protector of the elect of God) has been removed, Antichrist will take his seat in the Temple, demanding the worship of the world. This will truly initiate the fiery testing that comes upon the elect of God. The test that determines who the real elect of God truly are. The test that will separate the wheat from the tares. By this, the household of faith will be purified, and then the wicked of the world will be destroyed (1 Peter 4:17). For this reason, once again the Seraphim initiates the "going forth" of the fourth horseman, permitting the "hot coal" of Isaiah 6:6 to be applied to the compromising church of the last days.

13-14 According to Matthew 24:9, what is the very next event that occurs after the beginning birth pangs (v. 8)? (p. 249)

13-15 And according to Matthew 24:9, why are the elect of God killed? (p. 249)

13-16 According to Matthew 24:9, 12, what is the result of this direct persecution of the church in general? (p. 249)

13-17 According to the description of the condition of the seven churches listed in the book of Revelation (chapters 2-3), and the condition of the church described in 2 Timothy 3:1-5, what is the condition of the church at large that permits "many" to "fall away" and "most people's love [to] grow cold"?

13-18 According to Revelation 6:7,8, when compared with Matthew 24:9, 15, 21,22, what does the fourth horseman represent, and with what end-time event described by Christ, does the fourth horseman directly relate to? (p. 249)

13-19 What then is the choice that the church in general will make during the fiery testing (the days of the Great Tribulation), and what will be the results of their choice? (p. 249)

13-20 According to Revelation 6:7, who sends or permits the fourth horseman to go out into the world, accomplishing his purposes of purification of the church? (p. 249)

13-21 According to Revelation 6:8, the fourth horseman has authority over a "fourth of the earth." Knowing that the "household of faith" will be judged during the fiery testing that precedes the wrath of God (see 1 Pet. 4:16,17), the "fourth of the earth" that Satan seeks to destroy will represent whom? (p. 250)

13-22 Therefore, according to Matthew 13:30, what is taking place during the fourth seal when many die, when many fall away, and when their love for Christ grows cold? (p. 249)

13-23 According to Revelation 6:8, why does Hades (Hell) follow after Death? (p. 250)

13-24 According to Revelation 6:8, the method of death that will come to those who refuse to worship Antichrist will be three-fold. First will be the "sword." In the context of Revelation 13:7,10 when compared to Mark 13:11,12, what might we assume that "sword" refers to? (p. 251)

13-25 Antichrist's second method of killing those who choose loyalty to Christ rather than loyalty to Antichrist will be "with famine." In the context of the third seal, worldwide famine, and Revelation 13:16-17, what might we assume "famine" refers to? (p. 251)

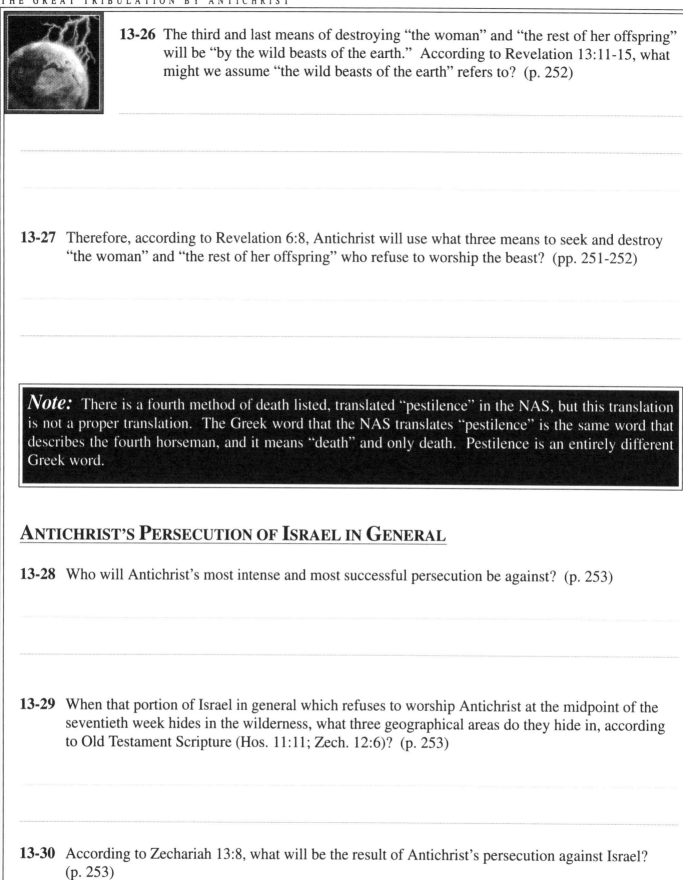

13-26 The third and last means of destroying "the woman" and "the rest of her offspring" will be "by the wild beasts of the earth." According to Revelation 13:11-15, what might we assume "the wild beasts of the earth" refers to? (p. 252)

13-27 Therefore, according to Revelation 6:8, Antichrist will use what three means to seek and destroy "the woman" and "the rest of her offspring" who refuse to worship the beast? (pp. 251-252)

Note: There is a fourth method of death listed, translated "pestilence" in the NAS, but this translation is not a proper translation. The Greek word that the NAS translates "pestilence" is the same word that describes the fourth horseman, and it means "death" and only death. Pestilence is an entirely different Greek word.

ANTICHRIST'S PERSECUTION OF ISRAEL IN GENERAL

13-28 Who will Antichrist's most intense and most successful persecution be against? (p. 253)

13-29 When that portion of Israel in general which refuses to worship Antichrist at the midpoint of the seventieth week hides in the wilderness, what three geographical areas do they hide in, according to Old Testament Scripture (Hos. 11:11; Zech. 12:6)? (p. 253)

13-30 According to Zechariah 13:8, what will be the result of Antichrist's persecution against Israel? (p. 253)

13-31 According to Zechariah 14:2, what percentage of the Jewish inhabitants of Jerusalem will remain in Jerusalem, choosing to bow down to Antichrist rather than flee into hiding? (p. 251)

CERTAIN JEWISH WITNESSES

13-32 Who is the special group described in Matthew 10:16, 17, 21-23, what are they doing, and when? (p. 254-255)

13-33 Looking again at Matthew 10:16,17, 21-23, what should this group of faithful Jewish witnesses be prepared to encounter, and for how long? (p. 255)

13-34 Looking again at Matthew 10:23, how do we know this passage refers specifically to the last days?

FIFTH SEAL MARTYRS

13-35 Who are the fifth seal martyrs (Rev. 6:9-11)? (p. 255)

13-36 Who may also be included among the fifth seal martyrs? (p. 256)

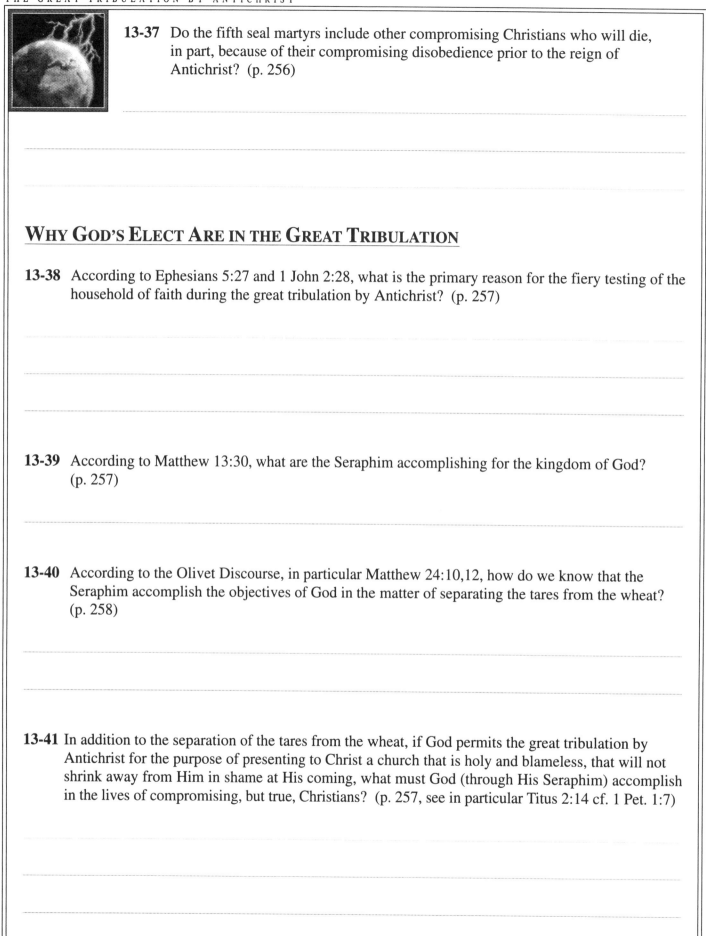

13-37 Do the fifth seal martyrs include other compromising Christians who will die, in part, because of their compromising disobedience prior to the reign of Antichrist? (p. 256)

WHY GOD'S ELECT ARE IN THE GREAT TRIBULATION

13-38 According to Ephesians 5:27 and 1 John 2:28, what is the primary reason for the fiery testing of the household of faith during the great tribulation by Antichrist? (p. 257)

13-39 According to Matthew 13:30, what are the Seraphim accomplishing for the kingdom of God? (p. 257)

13-40 According to the Olivet Discourse, in particular Matthew 24:10,12, how do we know that the Seraphim accomplish the objectives of God in the matter of separating the tares from the wheat? (p. 258)

13-41 In addition to the separation of the tares from the wheat, if God permits the great tribulation by Antichrist for the purpose of presenting to Christ a church that is holy and blameless, that will not shrink away from Him in shame at His coming, what must God (through His Seraphim) accomplish in the lives of compromising, but true, Christians? (p. 257, see in particular Titus 2:14 cf. 1 Pet. 1:7)

13-42 What are three reasons the author suggests, as to why God allows the true Christian to suffer? (pp. 258-259)

1.

2.

3.

FIFTH SEAL CONDITIONS MET

13-43 What major end-time event is occurring when the fifth seal is opened? (p. 261)

13-44 According to Revelation 6:10, had the wrath of God already started? (p. 262)

13-45 Why are the Seraphim not involved with oversight of the fifth seal? (p. 262)

13-46 According to Revelation 6:11, why is the fifth seal considered a condition that must be met before the wrath of God can begin with the opening of the large scroll? (p. 262)

13-47 According to Matthew 24:36, when compared with verses 21,22, when will the "number of their brethren . . . be completed also"?

NEW TESTAMENT EXPECTANCY VS. BIBLICAL REALITY

13-48 What did the early church not understand about Daniel 9:24 that gave them such a strong sense of expectancy in relationship to the return of Christ? (p. 263)

13-49 Why did the words of Jesus in John 21:21-23a give expectation to the early church regarding the coming of Christ? (p. 263)

13-50 What did many in the early church expect to be the next prophetic event? (p. 263)

13-51 Looking at Acts 1:6,7 and John 21:22,23, what is the general point being made? (p. 264)

13-52 According to 2 Thessalonians 2:3,4 and 2 Peter 3:3,8,9, what is the clear teaching of Scripture for the church in every age? (pp. 264-265)

13-53 Why do Christ and the writers of the New Testament use verbs in the present tense and pronouns in the first or second person when referring to the second coming of Christ? (pp. 265-266)

Personal Notes & Quotes:

CHAPTER
FOURTEEN

THE SIGN OF THE END OF THE AGE

F **CHAPTER FOCUS:**

In this chapter you will gain a clear understanding of Christ's answer to His disciples concerning the end of the age. You will understand the connection between the "day of the Lord" and the "end of the age," and you will see how specific signs relate to these specific events.

There will be three separate military campaigns that play an important part of your prophetic study. You will learn to distinguish between the three campaigns, avoiding much of the confusion that limits one's understanding of the last days.

R **Read chapter 14 of *The Sign* before answering the following questions.**

TIMELESS QUESTIONS

14-1 What three questions do the disciples ask in Matthew 24:3, and to what do these questions refer? (pp. 268; 497 endnote 1)

1.

2.

3.

14-2 In what two critical New Testament passages are these three questions answered? (p. 497 endnote 1)

14-3 In reference to Passover Week, just before the crucifixion of Christ, when was the Olivet Discourse given the disciples of Christ? (p. 268)

14-4 Why is the timing of the Olivet Discourse important to our discussion of end times? (p. 268)

14-5 Therefore, when the disciples asked for a sign concerning the "end of the age," according to Matthew 13:40, the "end of the age" referred to when?

14-6 Burning the tares at the end of the age was another reference to what? (see in particular 2 Pet. 3:7,10)

14-7 Were the disciples of Christ aware of Christ's teaching concerning the meaning of the end of the age? (see Matthew 13:36)

14-8 Why is the order of these two questions so significant, especially when compared to Luke 17:26-30? (p. 268)

14-9 What is Christ's specific warning to the church in Matthew 24:23-26? (p. 269)

WHAT WILL BE THE SIGN?

14-10 According to Matthew 24:29, cf. verse 22, when will the sign of the end of the age occur? (pp. 270-271)

14-11 What is the root Greek word translated "cut short," and what, in reality, does it really mean? (p. 497 endnote 2)

14-12 In the context of the second half of the seventieth week, does the text in Matthew 24:22, 29 say that the second half of the seventieth week (i.e. 42 months) is "cut short," or is it the time of great tribulation that is "cut short"? (p. 497 endnote 2)

14-13 If the counterfeit signs created by the false christs and false prophets will be stunningly impressive (see Matthew 24:24 and Revelation 13:13), according to Matthew 24:29, what is the true sign that will mark the end of the age? (p. 270)

14-14 What is the sign that Isaiah 13:10; 34:4 and Joel 2:31; 3:15 give which would precede the day of the Lord? (p. 270)

14-15 Why are Joel 2:30,31 and 3:14-16 significant? (p. 270)

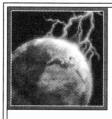

14-16 Is it fair to assume then that the sign that Christ refers to as the sign of the end of the age, is the same sign that the prophets foretold would occur just prior to the day of the Lord?

14-17 Putting Matthew 24:29 and Joel 2:31 together, specifically when will the sign of the end of the age occur in relationship to the great tribulation of Antichrist and the wrath of God during the day of the Lord? (p. 270)

14-18 In addition to the sign of the end of the age, what is the second sign that Christ speaks of in Matthew 24:30? (p. 270)

14-19 Where and when will "the sign of the Son of Man" (Matthew 24:30) appear? (pp. 270-271)

14-20 In summary, what three things can we conclude from what Christ has to say concerning these two specific signs? (p. 271)

1.

2.

3.

CHAPTER 14 FOURTEEN

14-21 What is the major theological significance of the above conclusions? (p. 271)

14-22 As a side question, what did we learn in the last chapter concerning the fifth seal that is the condition necessary for God to cut short the great tribulation by Antichrist? (see Rev. 6:11)

14-23 According to Luke 21:25-28, how will the non-believers respond to these two specific signs? (p. 272)

14-24 According to Luke 21:28, how will the believers respond to the signs? (p. 272)

As "That Day" Approaches

14-25 According to Revelation 14:9-11, why will the world know that the judgment of God is about to begin when they see the signs in the heaven? (p. 272)

14-26 Looking at 2 Thessalonians 2:10-12, what are two reasons that the angelic warnings will go unheeded? (p. 272)

1.

2.

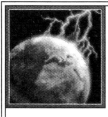

THE JEHOSHAPHAT CAMPAIGN

14-27 According to Joel 3:9, 12-16, what major event occurs in Israel, just before the sign of the day of the Lord is given in the heavenlies? (p. 274)

14-28 According to Joel 3:1,2, for what purpose are the nations brought into the valley of Jehoshaphat? (p. 274)

14-29 For this reason then, what title does the author give to this military campaign? (p. 274)

14-30 What are the three military campaigns that take place during the end times? (pp. 274-275)

1.

2.

3.

14-31 When does the Jerusalem Campaign take place, and what is its particular significance? (p. 275)

14-32 When does the Jehoshaphat Campaign take place, and what is its particular significance? (p. 275)

14-33 When does Armageddon take place, and what is its significance? (p. 275)

THE SIXTH SEAL

14-34 With what we have learned previously in this chapter, what is the significance of the sixth seal as described in Revelation 6:12-17? (p. 276)

14-35 Pretribulationalists who desire to make the entire seventieth week the wrath of God, attack what specific word in this critical sixth seal passage? (p. 499 endnote 5)

14-36 Define the meaning of the Greek word *ēlthen,* which is translated "has come" in Revelation 6:17. (pp. 277, 499-500 endnote 5)

14-37 What comparable Scripture passage also uses the same exact word, *ēlthen*, in the same exact manner? (p. 500 endnote 5)

14-38 What are the similarities in the use of the word *ēlthen* in the two passages? (p. 500 endnote 5)

Personal Notes & Quotes:

CHAPTER FIFTEEN

THE SIGN OF CHRIST'S COMING

F **CHAPTER FOCUS:**

You will now turn your attention to the second sign asked of Christ by His disciples, the sign of His coming, the sign that will be seen immediately after the first sign is given, announcing the return of Christ in judgment (the sign of the end of the age). You will learn the significance of this unbelievable sign, its Old Testament background, and you will see how it directly relates to the sign of the end of the age.

R **Read chapter 15 of *The Sign* before answering the following questions.**

SUPERNATURAL BRILLIANCE

15-1 According to Matthew 24:27, 30, what is the sign of Christ's coming? (p. 279)

15-2 According to Matthew 24:30 and Titus 2:13, what is the lighting a reference to? (p. 281)

15-3 What is the contrasting effect between the sign of the end of the age and the sign of Christ's coming? (p. 280)

15-4 According to Revelation 1:7, why will Christ's return be anything but secret and unobtrusive? (p. 280)

THE GLORIOUS APPEARING OF CHRIST

15-5 What is the Greek word rendered "is revealed" in Luke 17:30, and what idea is expressed in the more complete understanding of this word? (p. 281)

15-6 What is the Greek word and its meaning which is translated "appearing" in 2 Timothy 4:1, 8? (p. 281)

15-7 What is the Greek word and its meaning which is translated "appears" in 1 John 2:28? (p. 281)

15-8 Putting all these different Greek words together, what is the underlying thrust of these terms together? (p. 281)

15-9 In relationship to God's glory, how does Jude 24; 1 Peter 5:1, and Colossians 3:4 describe that believers will share in that glory? (p. 282)

15-10 What are some of the Old Testament passages that reveal that Messiah will come "in glory" to judge the world, restore the nation Israel, and establish His earthly kingdom? (pp. 282-283)

GOD'S GLORY IN ANCIENT ISRAEL

15-11 According to Ezekiel 11:22,23, what two separate stages were recorded, describing the departure of God's glory from Israel? (p. 284)

15-12 What are the two stages of the return of God's glory as described in Ezekiel 43:2-4? (pp. 284-285)

YOUR REDEMPTION DRAWETH NIGH

15-13 With the two past chapters in mind, the sign of the end of the age and the sign of Christ's coming, read Luke 21:25-28, and in your own words describe the reaction to these two signs by the kingdom of darkness — the lost world who will face the judgment of God — and by the kingdom of God — the true, living church looking for the return of Christ before the judgment begins.

Personal Notes & Quotes:

CHAPTER
SIXTEEN

THE PREWRATH RAPTURE OF THE CHURCH: PART I

F **CHAPTER FOCUS:**

In this study you will be looking at one of the most important chapters in *The Sign*. You will carefully analyze the prewrath Rapture position of Christ's return and see why it is the only biblical position clearly defended by Scripture, if Scripture is to be understood in its most natural, normal, and customary — literal — sense. You also will see why the imminent return of Christ is impossible, even today. You will again see that the rapture of the true, living church and the judgment of the kingdom of darkness will be back-to-back events, bringing to an end the persecution by Antichrist. Finally, you will gain a better understanding of why the Olivet Discourse is so relevant to the church and how, when compared to the classic Rapture passage outlined in 1 Thessalonians 4 (likewise for the church), the incredible similarities demand that both passages refer to exactly the same event.

R **Read chapter 16 of *The Sign* before answering the following questions.**

16-1   To what key passages do we look to best determine the timing of Christ's second coming? (p. 289)

16-2   Why can we expect all the prophecies concerning Christ's second coming to be fulfilled literally and completely? (p. 289)

16-3   What is the essence of the prewrath position concerning the rapture of the church? (p. 290)

16-4 In our study of the timing of the Rapture, what are the two most important aspects of Christ's return that the faithful church must remember? (p. 291)

1. _____

2. _____

RAPTURE AND WRATH ON THE SAME DAY

16-5 What do pretribulationalist teach today concerning the imminency of Christ's return? (p. 291)

16-6 How do pretribulationalists describe their own pretribulational view? (p. 481 endnote 5)

16-7 What has made an imminent return of Christ impossible down through the ages until just recently? (p. 292)

TAUGHT SPECIFICALLY BY CHRIST

16-8 In what Scripture passage does Christ very clearly state that the Rapture and the wrath will occur on exactly the same day? (p. 292)

CHAPTER
16
SIXTEEN

16-9 What is the argument some pretribulationalists use from Genesis 7:1-4 to explain away the fact that the Rapture and the wrath will occur on the same day as taught by Christ in Luke 17:30? (pp. 293, 500 endnote 1)

16-10 But according to Genesis 7:11-13 and Luke 17:30, what are two major problems with this argument? (p. 293)

16-11 Looking at Matthew 24:3, how do we know that the disciples understood the sequence of events that were to occur back-to-back? (pp. 293-294)

CONFIRMED BY PETER

16-12 How does Christ illustrate this truth in Matthew 24:37-41 and then reconfirm this truth through the writings of His apostle, Peter, in 2 Peter 2:5-9?

16-13 In Peter's confirmation of this truth in 2 Peter 2:9, what is a better translation of the word translated "temptation"? (pp. 294, 469-470 endnote 2, 500 endnote 3)

ONE "TAKEN" AND THE OTHER "LEFT"

16-14 According to Matthew 24:40,41 where is the one "taken" taken to, and where is the one "left" left at? (p. 295)

16-15 Define the Greek word *paralambanō* which is translated "taken" in Matthew 24:40,41. (pp. 295, 501-502 endnote 5)

16-16 In what classic Rapture passage does Jesus use this same Greek word, *paralambanō*? (p. 295)

16-17 Would it not be confusing if the Lord used *paralambanō* in this classic Rapture passage and actually intended it to describe something totally different in Matthew 24:40,41? (pp. 295-296)

CONFIRMED BY PAUL

16-18 After describing the Rapture in 1 Thessalonians 4:13-17, when does Paul in 1 Thessalonians 5:2, say the Rapture will occur? (pp. 296-297)

16-19 In 1 Thessalonians 5:2, what significance is there to the phrase, "thief in the night," and how is it used in other Scripture? (p. 297)

CHAPTER
16
SIXTEEN

16-20 In light of this study, in that it pertains to the rapture of the church and God's judgment of the wicked, what is our only conclusion? (p. 297)

16-21 Does the teaching of Christ in Luke 17:26-30 verify this truth, that the coming of Christ and the beginning of God's judgment of the wicked will occur on the very same day? (p. 297)

16-22 According to Matthew 24:29,30 cf. Joel 3:12-15, when then can the elect of God look for the two signs that will signal the end of the age and the coming of Christ? (p. 297)

16-23 According to Matthew 24:29 cf. verse 22, when will these signs occur in the heavenlies? (p. 497 endnote 2)

CHRIST'S COMING FOLLOWS THE GREAT TRIBULATION

16-24 Therefore, according to Matthew 24:21-31, should the church be prepared to enter the great tribulation and why? (p. 298)

THE COMING (PAROUSIA) OF CHRIST

16-25 Define the Greek words (*parousia*, *hēkō*, and *erchomai*) translated "coming."
(pp. 298, 502 endnote 6)

1.

2.

3.

16-26 In relationship to Christ's second coming, explain the significance of the Greek word *parousia*.
(p. 298)

TAUGHT SPECIFICALLY BY CHRIST

Note: What follows will be a defense of the fact that the rapture of the elect of God and God's wrath against the wicked that remain, is the central focus of the Olivet Discourse of Christ to His disciples, soon to have the responsibility of building the church after the crucifixion and resurrection of Christ. In addition, it will be seen that Paul taught exactly the same truths to the Church of Thessalonica when confusion arose concerning the return of Christ, and John describes exactly the same sequence of events in the book of Revelation. Therefore, the Olivet Discourse is at the very heart of the teachings concerning the rapture of the church before the judgment of God upon the kingdom of darkness.

However, in an attempt to confuse the clear teaching of Christ concerning the timing of the return of Christ, i.e. the sign of Christ's coming and the end of the age, many pretribulationalists maintain that the book of Matthew was not written for the church, but only for unsaved Israel that will not come to know Christ until after the seventieth week is complete! Therefore, all of the events described in the Olivet Discourse occur in and around the battle of Armageddon at the close of the seventieth week with no consideration whatsoever being given to the church or her rapture before the wrath. This could not be further from the truth, and for that reason, before we continue with an analysis of several critical verses taken from the Olivet Discourse, we must see why the Olivet Discourse is for the church, not for unsaved Israel.

16-27 Is the book of Matthew written for unsaved Israel or the church?
(p. 503 endnote 7)

16-28 Is the Great Commission recorded in Matthew 28:19,20 instructions for unsaved Israel or for the church? (p. 503 endnote 7)

16-29 What phrase in the Great Commission is particularly significant in proving that the book of Matthew must be written for the church? (p. 503 endnote 7)

16-30 In what Gospels do we find Jesus using the term "church"? (p. 503 endnote 7)

16-31 When, in relationship to Passover Week just prior to the crucifixion of Christ, was the Olivet Discourse of Jesus given to His disciples? (p. 503 endnote 7)

16-32 According to John 14:1-3, what other important event (other than the institution of the Lord's Supper) did Jesus speak about to His disciples on the sixth day of Passover Week? (p.503 endnote 7)

16-33 What then is an obvious conclusion concerning the instruction given to Christ's disciples in the Olivet Discourse? (p. 503 endnote 7)

16-34 Continuing on now with the Olivet Discourse of Christ, what is the general sequence of events that Jesus describes in Matthew 24? (p. 299)

16-35 According to Matthew 24:29 when did Jesus say His *parousia* — His coming when He would gather together (rapture) His living elect — would take place? (p. 299)

CONFIRMED BY PAUL

Note: Therefore, Christ taught that His coming would occur when He cuts short the great tribulation by Antichrist, who has been demanding the worship of the world since the midpoint of the seventieth week. In a parallel passage, this one taught by Paul to the church of Thessalonica, we see the identical sequence of events described, even though the emphasis and words may be different. The church of Thessalonica had been led to believe that they had missed the rapture of the church described by Paul in his first letter to the church in Thessalonica and that the day of the Lord had begun, leaving them behind to go through the wrath of God. In order to correct this faulty teaching, Paul writes Second Thessalonians, the critical issue being the clarification of exactly when the second coming of Christ (and thus, the beginning of the day of the Lord) would commence (2 Thess. 2:1-2).

16-36 Carefully examine 2 Thessalonians 2:1-9, as it is an extremely important prophetic passage concerning the return of Christ. Second Thessalonians 2:1 associates what two events with the day of the Lord in verse 2? (pp. 300-301)

16-37 What, according to verse 3a, must take place before the events outlined in the preceding two verses, 1 and 2? (p. 301)

16-38 Looking at verse 3b of 2 Thessalonians 2, what is the next event that must occur first? (p. 301)

16-39 In verse 4, what is the third event that must occur before our "gathering together" described in verses one and two? (p. 301)

16-40 According to verses 6,7, who has restrained the persecution of Antichrist up until this specific point in time? (p. 301)

16-41 What event, according to verse 8, finally brings an end to the persecution of Antichrist against the elect of God? (p. 301)

16-42 Give the parallels in the sequence of events of 2 Thessalonians 2:1-8, when compared to the sequence of events described by Christ in His Olivet Discourse, that demand that both accounts are referring to exactly the same event? (p. 301)

THE RAPTURE DESCRIBED

16-43 What four important truths about Christ's coming (parousia) are contained in Matthew 24:30,31? (p. 302)

1.

2.

3.

4.

16-44 Looking at 1 Thessalonians 4:15-17 — the classic New Testament Rapture passage — what four truths about Christ's return are stated again, paralleling our key passage taken from Matthew 24:30,31 in the previous question? (p. 302)

1.

2.

3.

4.

16-45 According to Matthew 13:30, 39, who will gather together the church from earth to meet our Lord in the clouds? (p. 302)

16-46 And comparing Scripture with Scripture, how does Matthew 16:27 confirm this fact?

16-47 How do the four events described in the classic Rapture passage (1 Thessalonians 4:13-17) compare with the events described in the Olivet Discourse (Matthew 24:30,31)? (p. 303)

16-48 What are three essential teachings of Scripture concerning the coming (*parousia*) of Christ we have learned in this chapter? (p. 303)

1.

2.

3.

CHAPTER
SEVENTEEN

THE PREWRATH RAPTURE OF THE CHURCH: PART II

F **CHAPTER FOCUS:**

In this chapter, you will continue to study the biblical evidence for the prewrath Rapture position. In particular, you will carefully consider what God's Word says about the great multitude in Revelation 7 and see how their identification perfectly reinforces the teaching of Christ in the Olivet Discourse and the teaching of Paul to the Thessalonians. More importantly, this chapter — along with the preceding one — will give you the tools to biblically defend the timing of Christ's return. So, go very carefully and think very clearly about the arguments that have been developed both in the last chapter and in this chapter as well. To be forewarned is to be forearmed.

R **Read chapter 17 of *The Sign* before answering the following questions.**

CONFIRMED BY REVELATION

Note: In the last chapter, you looked carefully at the teaching of Christ to His disciples, answering their questions concerning the sign of His coming (parousia) and the sign of the end of the age. Christ told His disciples not to be "misled" on this matter and then went on to carefully and clearly teach the soon-to-be church fathers that His return would occur when He cuts short the great tribulation of Antichrist against the elect of God. Several decades later, Paul needed to deal directly with the confusion concerning the coming (parousia) of Christ, our gathering together to Him, and the day of the Lord that would follow. And, like Christ, Paul tells the Thessalonians not to be "deceived" and then confirms exactly the same sequence of events that Christ had taught His disciples in the Olivet Discourse. First the apostasy, then the revealing of Antichrist, then the demands of Antichrist for the worship of the world, and finally the coming (parousia) of Christ when, in the context of the passage, the church will be gathered together to Christ and Antichrist will be brought to an end.

We now continue our study by looking at the teaching of Christ through the apostle John in the book of Revelation.

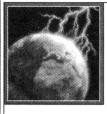

17-1 How does Revelation 6 harmonize with the sequence of events specifically outlined in the Olivet Discourse? (p. 306)

17-2 How do the events described in Revelation 7, fit chronologically into Revelation chapters 6 and 8? (p. 306)

Note: Keeping in mind the fact that chapter 7 is an interlude between the breaking of the sixth seal (the sign of the end of the age) and the breaking of the seventh seal (which will open the large scroll and initiate the day of the Lord), let us now look carefully at the all-important interlude between these two specific seal events.

THE GREAT HEAVENLY MULTITUDE

17-3 What three different groups are present in the heavenlies when the great multitude arrives (Revelation 7:9, 14), according to Revelation 7:11? (p. 307)

17-4 Who is noticeably absent from this group of onlookers?

17-5 Revelation 7:13b asks the question concerning the great multitude, "who are they"? Who are we told in verse 9 that this great multitude is? (p. 307)

17-6 Comparing Scripture to Scripture, where else is this identical description used in the book of Revelation, and to whom does it clearly refer? (pp. 307-308)

17-7 In Revelation 7:13b, the question is asked, "and from where have they come"? According to verse 14, where does this great multitude come from? (p. 307)

17-8 All of the other seal events have paralleled the Olivet Discourse, Christ being the author of both end-time instructions. Who then, according to the Olivet Discourse of Christ, must this great multitude be? (p. 308)

Note: In an attempt to confuse the obvious, pretribulationalists will tell you that this great multitude does not all arrive at one time, but rather, is a group of Gentile martyrs that is getting larger and larger as the great tribulation progresses and more Gentile converts are being slain by Antichrist. However, integrity with the Greek text will not permit that position.

17-9 Explain why the Greek term *hoi erchomai*, which is translated in Revelation 7:14 as "the ones who come," does not describe a continual coming, rather than a one time event. (pp. 506-507 endnote 2)

1.

2.

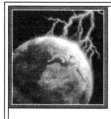

Note: To justify this ever-growing multitude in the heavenlies, the pretribulationists teach that this great multitude must represent Gentile martyrs that are saved during a tremendous Gentile revival that takes place during the seventieth week of Daniel. Again, using their own system of thinking, this position makes no sense whatsoever.

17-10 How does this explanation concerning the great multitude being Gentile converts during the great tribulation by Antichrist, contradict the very premise upon which pretribulationalism is built? (p. 508 endnote 3)

17-11 According to 2 Thessalonians 2:4,11,12, what is the biblical reason why there will not be a great Gentile revival during the seventieth week? (p. 508 endnote 3)

17-12 Is there any evidence in the book of Revelation of a great revival during the seventieth week (see in particular Rev. 9:20,21)? (p. 508 endnote 3)

17-13 In contrast to the position taken by the pretribulationalist, what inescapable proof do we have that this great multitude must be the church? (pp. 308-309)

17-14 According to Revelation 20:4, when will the martyred saints receive their resurrection bodies? (pp. 308-309)

17-15 According to Revelation 20:11-15 and John 5:29, when will the unsaved be resurrected? (p. 509 endnote 5)

17-16 According to 1 Corinthians 15:52, how soon after the Rapture will the elect, both the dead and the living, receive their resurrection bodies? (pp. 309-310)

17-17 Therefore, as a result of your study of the great multitude of Revelation 7, and then comparing these results with the Olivet Discourse of Christ, and the teachings of Paul to the Thessalonians, what is the first of the eight logical conclusions which we come to concerning who this great multitude must be? (p. 310)

17-18 What is the second conclusion? (p. 310)

17-19 What is the third conclusion? (p. 310)

17-20   What is the <u>fourth conclusion</u>? (p. 310)

17-21   What is the <u>fifth conclusion</u>? (p. 310)

17-22   What is the <u>sixth conclusion</u>? (p. 310)

17-23   What is the <u>seventh conclusion</u>? (p. 310)

17-24   What is the <u>only logical conclusion</u> then, that we can come to concerning the identity of this great multitude? (pp. 310-311)

THE "DEAD IN CHRIST" RISE FIRST

17-25   Who are the "dead in Christ" that are resurrected at the same time the living church is raptured (see 1 Thess. 4:16-17)? (pp. 311-312)

17-26   What three "key" Old Testament passages show specifically that the Old Testament saint is resurrected with the New Testament saint when the church is raptured? (pp. 312-313)

17-27 Although these three Old Testament passages (mentioned in 17-26) are not identical, how do they, when put together, confirm the New Testament sequence we have already studied? (p. 314)

THE TRUMPET OF GOD

17-28 As we worked through earlier in this study guide (See chapter 8, questions 12 and 13), why is the "last trumpet of God" mentioned in connection with the rapture of the church (1 Corinthians 15:52 and 1 Thessalonians 4:16) not the seventh trumpet judgment (the last trumpet judgment) recorded in the book of Revelation? (pp. 509-510 endnote 7)

17-29 What in reality is the last trumpet blown by anyone prior to the Millennium? (pp. 509-510 endnote 7)

17-30 According to Zechariah 9:14-16 when is the only other time God blows the trumpet? (pp. 509-510 endnote 7)

17-31 Therefore, in light of the foregoing, what significance is there to the fact that the 1 Thessalonians 4:16 text refers to the trumpet as "the trumpet of God"? (pp. 509-510 endnote 7)

THE SEALING OF THE 144,000

17-32 According to Revelation 7:1-4, when are the 144,000 sealed? (p. 314-315)

17-33 According to Revelation 9:4, where will this "seal of God" be displayed on the person of the 144,000? (p. 315)

17-34 According to Revelation 9:4, what is one direct benefit of the sealing of the 144,000? (p. 315)

17-35 According to Ezekiel 20:35-37, what is the most important benefit of the sealing of the 144,000 remnant who are in hiding in the wilderness of Edom? (pp. 314-315)

17-36 According to Revelation 14:4, why are the 144,000 sealed at this particular time rather than being raptured with the church? (pp. 314-315)

CHAPTER
EIGHTEEN

THE DAY OF THE LORD

F **CHAPTER FOCUS:**

In this study you will examine in more detail one of the most critical prophetic events of the end times, the day of the Lord. The purpose of this chapter is to give you a better overall understanding of the purpose of the day of the Lord, in general, and the severity of the judgment it will represent. In addition, you will see why God permits the natural line of Abraham to go through these terrible days, and finally, how God handles Antichrist during this time when "the Lord alone will be exalted" (Isa. 2:17).

R **Read chapter 18 of *The Sign* before answering the following questions.**

18-1 Is the day of the Lord one or two separate events that occur in the last days?   (p. 511 endnotes 1-2)

_____

_____

THE BEGINNING OF JUDGMENT

18-2 According to Zephaniah 1:14-18, how severe in terms of human life, will the day of the Lord be? (p. 321)

_____

_____

18-3 According to 2 Peter 3:10, how severe in terms of physical damage, is the day of the Lord? (p. 321)

_____

_____

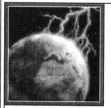

2 PETER 3 AND THE DAY OF THE LORD

> *Note:* The most direct instruction concerning the day of the Lord is found in 2 Peter 3, and yet there are many who would try to put the event described in this passage, at the end of the Millennium rather at the time of Christ's return. The 2 Peter 3 passage is a critical passage, not only concerning the day of the Lord but end-time events in general, especially as it relates to the new heavens and earth discussed in more detail in chapter 22 of this study guide. Therefore, we must first understand — and be able to defend — why this critical passage can only refer to the one and only day of the Lord that occurs at the coming "parousia" of Christ, before the Millennium, not at the end of it.

18-4 Six reasons are given by the author as to why 2 Peter 3 must be referring to the day of the Lord that occurs at the rapture of the church, not some second day of the Lord that will occur at the end of the Millennium. Give the <u>first reason</u>. (p. 511 endnote 2)

18-5 Give the <u>second reason</u>. (pp. 511-512 endnote 2)

18-6 Give the <u>third reason</u>. (p. 512 endnote 2)

18-7 Give the <u>fourth reason</u>. (p. 512 endnote 2)

CHAPTER 18 EIGHTEEN

18-8 Give the <u>fifth reason</u>. (p. 512 endnote 2)

18-9 Give the <u>sixth reason</u>. (p. 512 endnote 2)

A FIERY, SUPERNATURAL JUDGMENT

18-10 Since God has promised never again to destroy the world by water, according to 2 Peter 3:7 what kind of judgment will the world face during the day of the Lord? (p. 322)

18-11 According to 2 Peter 3:10, how severe, in terms of physical damage, will the day of the Lord be? (p. 321)

18-12 Because of the extensive damage that will occur during the day of the Lord, according to 2 Peter 3:13 what has God promised to do for those who survive God's judgment and become participants of Christ's millennial rule upon earth?

18-13 God has used natural disasters and human means as instruments of judgment in the past. When God destroys the heavens and the earth during the day of the Lord, what means will He use? (p. 322)

THE OPENING OF THE SEVENTH SEAL

18-14 If the day of the Lord's wrath begins with the opening of the large scroll, what seal should evidence some of the truths already discussed concerning the day of the Lord? (p. 323)

Note: As initially established in chapter 10 under the subtitle of "The Large Scroll," the large scroll cannot be opened until all seven seals are opened first. As carefully explained in chapter 10 of this study guide, when the seventh and last seal is broken open by the "Lion of Judah," then the large scroll can be opened that initiates the wrath of God upon the earth's wicked, during a time known as "the day of the Lord."

18-15 According to Revelation 8:2, who holds the seven trumpets associated with the seventh seal and how is this significant according to Matthew 13:37-42? (p. 324)

18-16 According to Revelation 8:5, what significant action is taken by "another angel" before the seven angels with the seven trumpets begin to sound, and what is the significance of this action? (p. 324)

18-17 After reading Revelation chapters 8-9, which of the six trumpet judgments involve fire? (p. 325)

18-18 According to Jesus' explanation of the parable of the wheat and the tares (Matthew 13:37-40), who are we told will be the reapers of that harvest when the tares are burned at the end of the age? (p. 324)

18-19 Who administers the judgments (both trumpet and bowl judgments) associated with the seventh seal (see Revelation 8:6; 15:8), and what can we conclude by this fact?

GOD'S PURPOSE FOR THE DAY OF THE LORD

18-20 What are the two primary purposes of the day of the Lord?   (p. 326)

18-21 What is the primary reason for God's wrath against the ungodly as evidenced by Revelation 9:20,21? (p. 326)

18-22 According to Isaiah 1:24-28, for what specific purpose does God use the day of the Lord for Israel? (p. 326)

18-23 According to Amos 5:18,19, then, the day of the Lord will be what sort of day to the nation of Israel?

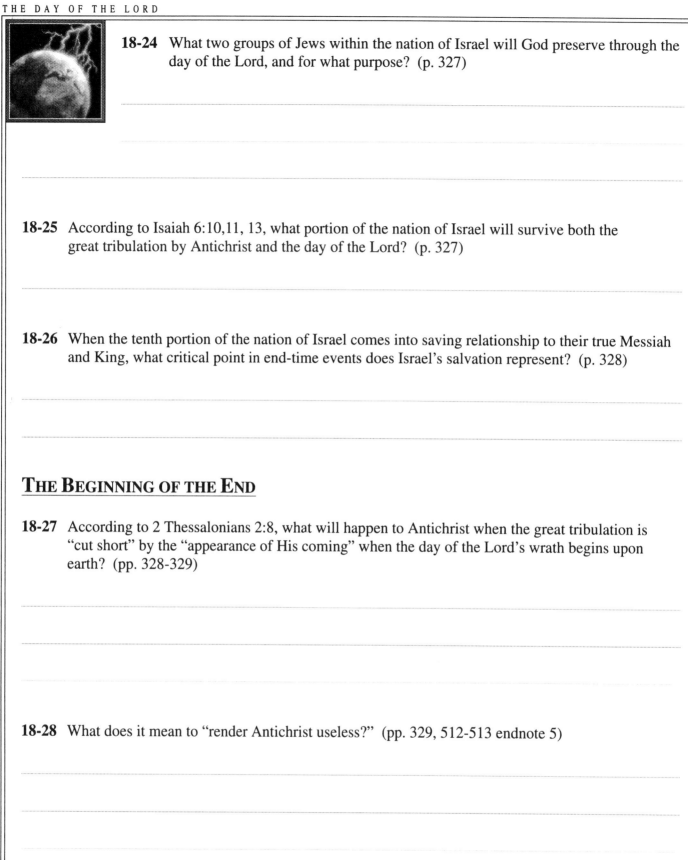

18-24 What two groups of Jews within the nation of Israel will God preserve through the day of the Lord, and for what purpose? (p. 327)

18-25 According to Isaiah 6:10,11, 13, what portion of the nation of Israel will survive both the great tribulation by Antichrist and the day of the Lord? (p. 327)

18-26 When the tenth portion of the nation of Israel comes into saving relationship to their true Messiah and King, what critical point in end-time events does Israel's salvation represent? (p. 328)

THE BEGINNING OF THE END

18-27 According to 2 Thessalonians 2:8, what will happen to Antichrist when the great tribulation is "cut short" by the "appearance of His coming" when the day of the Lord's wrath begins upon earth? (pp. 328-329)

18-28 What does it mean to "render Antichrist useless?" (pp. 329, 512-513 endnote 5)

THE JEWISH COUNTERATTACK

18-29 According to Zechariah 14:12-14a, when does the remnant of Israel — the clans of Judah in hiding — retaliate against Antichrist, and what historical event does this parallel? (pp. 329-330)

THE FINAL EVENT OF THE SEVENTIETH WEEK

18-30 According to Revelation 11:7-10, what is the final event of the seventieth week? (pp. 330)

18-31 What is the world's response to this final event of the seventieth week? (pp. 331-332)

18-32 What are the only two things that God will allow Antichrist to do after he has been "rendered useless"? (p. 332)

1.

2.

THE FULFILLMENT OF DANIEL 9:24

18-33 How does the prophecy in Daniel 9:24 relate to the end of the seventieth week? (p. 333)

1.

2.

3.

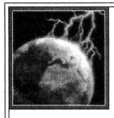

18-34 Even though the wrath of God is not yet complete when the seventieth week ends, what two significant events have now taken place? (p. 334)

1. _____

2. _____

CHAPTER
NINETEEN

THE MYSTERY OF GOD IS FINISHED

F **CHAPTER FOCUS:**

This is one of the most important chapters of our entire study together. In this study you will examine a new scroll, the little scroll, which initiates the events that immediately follow the close of the seventieth week. The culmination of the cosmic conflict will occur in the first thirty days that immediately follow the seventieth week, a time period called the reclamation period by the author. First you will come to understand what the "Mystery of God" is and how the mystery will be finished. In the process, you will trace the activities of Christ when He will quite literally set foot upon earth for the first time since New Testament days. And then, finally, you will see the fulfillment of the one event that Satan has feared most, God's reclaiming the rule over Earth back to Himself.

R **Read chapter 19 of *The Sign* before answering the following questions.**

THE SMALL SCROLL

> ***Note:*** The martyrdom of the two witnesses will mark the close of the seventieth week of Daniel. Israel's transgression will be finished, sin in the nation will be over, and from God's perspective they will have made proper atonement for sin. The close of the seventieth week marks the close of the large scroll. But there is still more. The time has come to bring in everlasting righteousness, to seal up vision and prophecy, and to anoint the most holy (see Daniel 9:24). Thus we turn to a new scroll, introduced to us in Revelation 10, the little scroll.

19-1 In the opinion of the author, what does the sweetness of the little book (scroll) mentioned in Revelation 10:10 refer to? (p. 336)

_____

_____

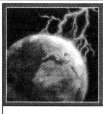

19-2 Then again, in the opinion of the author, what is the bitterness of the little book mentioned in the same passage referring to? (p. 336)

19-3 As mentioned in the note at the beginning of this chapter's study, the close of what significant end-time prophetic event will mark the close of the large scroll?

19-4 What, then, does the "little scroll" represent? (p. 336)

THE THIRTY-DAY RECLAMATION PERIOD

19-5 What three things are "reclaimed" during the thirty-day reclamation period? (pp. 336-337)

1.

2.

3.

19-6 Earlier in our study in chapter 5, we determined how many days there are in a prophetic year. How many are there? (pp. 89-90)

19-7 According to Daniel 12:11 (in conjunction with Daniel 9:27), there will be 1,290 days that are somehow associated with two key events that occur during the end times. What are these two events, and is our key passage making reference to "duration" or "interval"? (pp. 337-338)

1.

2.

19-8 When do the 1,290 days end in relationship to the seventieth week? (p. 338)

19-9 When does Daniel 12:11, therefore, tell us that Antichrist will be destroyed? (p. 338)

FORETOLD BY HOSEA

19-10 According to Hosea 5:15, Daniel 9:24 and Romans 11:25,26, when will all of Israel be saved? (p. 339)

19-11 According to Hosea 6:1-3, when compared with Daniel 9:24, when will Israel repent of her sin and be reunited spiritually with their Messiah? (p. 340)

19-12 According to Zechariah 12:10, how does Israel finally receive Jesus as their Messiah? (p. 340)

CHRIST'S PHYSICAL RETURN TO EARTH

19-13 If Israel is saved when they see Christ face to face, what then must first take place at the very beginning of the thirty-day reclamation period? (p. 340)

19-14 In the context of what we just learned, what is the meaning of Hebrews 9:28? (pp. 340, 514 endnote 2)

THE "STRONG ANGEL"

19-15 Who is the "strong angel" of Revelation 10? (p. 341)

19-16 In Revelation 10:2 the "strong angel" holds the open little scroll in his hand. What is a possible conclusion we can come to from this? (pp. 341-342)

19-17 Revelation 10:6 shows the strong angel making an oath in whose name? (p. 342)

19-18 According to Hebrews 6:13, does God ever swear in His own name? (p. 343)

19-19 Now, comparing Scripture with Scripture, to whom does Ezekiel's vision concerning a figure "with the appearance of a man" (1:26-28 cf. 8:2) refer to? (p. 331)

19-20 When Ezekiel's "figure with the appearance of a man" — Christ — is compared with John's "strong angel," what do we find? (p. 343)

19-21 What other Old Testament passage describing the appearance of the Lord bears a strong resemblance to John's description of the "strong angel" of Revelation 10? (p. 343)

19-22 Later, according to Daniel 12:7, what interesting thing do we find this "man dressed in linen" — Jehovah God — doing that exactly parallels our "strong angel" in Revelation 10? (p. 343)

19-23 One last parallel we must look at before we continue. How does the roar of the lion described in Revelation 10:3 parallel Old Testament teaching found in Hosea 11:10,11? (p. 344)

19-24 Finally, one last comment about John's "strong angel." According to Revelation 10:1, 5, where is this angel coming from and going to? (p. 344)

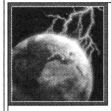

Note: The author recognizes that he has gone to some great lengths to show that John's "strong angel" is Christ, coming down to earth from heaven. Actually, in all my reading, no one has ever put all these issues together the way we have attempted to do in this chapter. For that reason I want you, the student, to have a strong biblical foundation for the incredible events that now occur during the next few days immediately following the close of the seventieth week and the return of Christ to earth for the salvation of Israel. This is the one event Satan has done all in his power to prevent because with the salvation of the remnant of Israel that survives the seventieth week, approximately 10% of the spiritual kingdom of God will be complete, and God Almighty will reclaim the physical rule over earth, bringing an end to Satan and his kingdom of darkness. Therefore, let us now look at, in detail, the incredible events that unfold during the first six days after the close of the seventieth week.

DAY ONE AND TWO: EDOM TO ISRAEL

19-25 Comparing Romans 11:26 to Isaiah 59:20, where will Christ be coming from and where will He be going when He physically returns to earth at the end of the seventieth week? (p. 344)

19-26 According to Isaiah 63:1-3 when compared with Revelation 12:6, when Christ physically returns to earth, where does He return to first, and why? (p. 344)

19-27 What is the significance of the blood stained garments of Christ mentioned in Isaiah 63:1-3? (p. 345)

19-28 According to verse one (Isaiah 63), what specific city in Edom is mentioned, out of which Christ is seen coming? (p. 345)

CHAPTER 19 NINETEEN

19-29 What Old Testament passage speaks directly to Israel's Messiah (as Lord and King) leading "the remnant" out of Bozrah, perfectly substantiating Isaiah 63:1-3? (p. 345)

19-30 The prophet Habakkuk also vividly describes Christ's coming from Edom. What two extremely significant truths do we find in Habakkuk 3:13? (p. 346)

1.

2.

DAY THREE: THE MYSTERY IS COMPLETE!

19-31 What is the mystery that John refers to in Revelation 10:7, when compared to Romans 11:25? (p. 348)

19-32 According to Hebrews 9:28, how will Israel respond? (p. 348)

19-33 According to Revelation 10:7, when will the mystery of God concerning the salvation of Israel be finished? (pp. 348-349)

19-34 According to Hosea 6:2, on exactly which day after the close of the seventieth week will Israel be saved? (p. 349)

19-35 What two groups will, in addition, come to a saving knowledge of Jesus Christ when they join Christ and "the woman" (the 144,000 first fruits) on their journey on foot from Edom to Jerusalem? (pp. 349-350)

1.

2.

19-36 According to Isaiah 35:8, what will the highway from Egypt and Assyria back to Jerusalem be called? (p. 350)

19-37 Who can travel on this highway? (p. 350)

19-38 According to Hosea 11:10 (when compared with Revelation 10:3), what will be the signal for the Jewish remnant hiding from Antichrist in Egypt and Assyria to come out and meet their Lord? (p. 350)

19-39 According to Zechariah 12:7-10, who will be the final group of Jews that will come to a saving knowledge of Christ? (p. 351)

19-40 In summary then, on which day after the close of the seventieth week will the Lord save the 10% remnant of Israel (other than the 144,000) that survives the seventieth week? (p. 352)

19-41 What, then, is the tremendous end-time significance of Israel's salvation — the completion of the mystery of God? (p. 351)

DAY FOUR: THE TWO WITNESSES' RESURRECTION

19-42 According to Revelation 11:11, what happens on the fourth day after the completion of the seventieth week and how does the world respond? (p. 352)

19-43 What are several reasons that we might suggest as to why God raised up the two witnesses and took them back to heaven at this precise time? (p. 352)

1.

2.

3.

4.

5.

19-44 According to Revelation 11:13, what takes place at the time of the resurrection of the two witnesses? (pp. 352-353)

DAY FIVE: THE SEVENTH TRUMPET!

19-45 According to Revelation 11:15-17, what is the next important event that takes place, and why does the author say that this event has "overwhelming significance"? (p. 353)

19-46 On what day does the author believe that the 7th trumpet will be blown? (p. 353)

19-47 Why is the sequence of events outlined in Revelation 11:14,18 so important? (p. 353)

19-48 How does Daniel 2:44 confirm the truth described in Revelation 11:15-19, that God Almighty reclaims the authority over earth before the final destruction of Antichrist and his nations? (p. 354)

19-49 According to Obadiah 21, who and where will the "deliverers" be when "the kingdom will be the Lord's"? (p. 354)

19-50 How does Revelation 14:1-3 reinforce this possibility? (p. 354)

19-51 According to Revelation 15:2-4 where the words of the "new song" of 14:3 are recorded, what is the title given to God Almighty? (p. 355)

19-52 Why is the author convinced that the "deliverers" will be singing the "Psalm of Ascension" as they ascend to the top of Mount Zion for this great event at the sounding of the seventh trumpet? (pp. 355, 515 endnote 5)

Note: As an aside, it is interesting to note that the Feast of Tabernacles occurs on the summit of Mount Zion exactly five days after Yom Kippur, the Day of Atonement. The parallels between the events of end-times and several of these critical Jewish holy days is incredible. Read the Epilogue of *The Sign* for a more in-depth discussion of this matter. The parallels one can make between the holy days and the end-times will not be gone into in depth in this study guide.

DAY SIX: REMNANT TO AZEL

19-53 According to Isaiah 26:20,21, what takes place on the sixth day after the close of the seventieth week? (pp. 355-356)

19-54 According to Zechariah 14:2-5, how and where will God preserve the believing remnant of Israel during the final wrath of God? (p. 356)

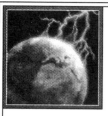

BEMA-SEAT JUDGMENT

19-55   According to the author, what event takes place next back in the heavenlies? (p. 357)

19-56   Who will participate in this bema-seat judgment? (p. 357)

19-57   What passage in the book of Revelation pinpoints the exact timing of the bema-seat judgment, and where, in the order of events described, does this judgment occur? (p. 358)

CHAPTER
TWENTY

THE FINAL WRATH OF GOD

F **CHAPTER FOCUS:**

In this study you will examine the events associated with the seventh trumpet judgment, and the final wrath of God — the seven bowl judgments and the climatic battle of Armageddon when Antichrist and the armies of the kingdom of darkness will be destroyed. In addition, you will study that great event that takes place in heaven while God is pouring out His final wrath upon the kingdom of darkness.

R **Read chapter 20 of *The Sign* before answering the following questions.**

20-1 According to Daniel 2:44, what is the sequence of events during the final outpouring of God's wrath? (p. 361)

....

....

....

A PREVIEW OF GOD'S JUDGMENT

20-2 What is the order of events that will happen, as outlined in Revelation 11:15-19? (p. 362)

1. ....

2. ....

3. ....

4. ....

5. ....

6. _____

7. _____

20-3 What is the significance of using the term "bowl" ("vial") in Revelation 15:7; 16:1? (pp. 363-364, 516 endnote 1)

_____

_____

_____

20-4 What are some of the Old Testament passages that would substantiate the "pouring out" of God's wrath during the final bowl judgments? (pp. 363-364)

_____

THE ARK OF THE COVENANT

20-5 According to Revelation 11:19, what occurs in heaven just preceding the final wrath of God? (p. 365)

_____

20-6 The timing of the reappearance of the ark after these thousands of years is significant in light of the events that have just transpired. What are the two events the author refers to? (p. 365)

1. _____

2. _____

20-7 What will the ark symbolize to Israel at this critical time in end-time events? (p. 365)

1. _____

2. _____

3. _____

4. _____

THE BOWL JUDGMENTS

Note: With the salvation of the remnant of Israel now history, with God Almighty having reclaimed the rule over earth at the seventh trumpet, with the remnant of Israel now safely tucked away in hiding, and with the appearance of the ark in the heavenlies, the time has come for God's final, destructive wrath upon the kingdom of darkness.

20-8 According to Revelation 15:1, what is the specific significance of the bowl judgments?

20-9 Because the bowl judgments are not initiated until after the seventieth week is complete, and because the abomination of desolation will last 1,290 days (Dan. 12:11), using simple mathematics, what does this tell us about the time frame associated with the final bowl judgments? (p. 366)

20-10 What is significant about the last three bowl judgments and the final battle of Armageddon? (p. 366)

20-11 Referring to Revelation 16:1,2, give a brief description of the first bowl judgment. (p. 367)

20-12 Referring to Revelation 16:3, give a brief description of the second bowl judgment. (p. 367)

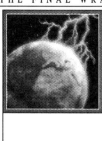

20-13 Referring to Revelation 16:4-7, give a brief description of the third bowl judgment. (p. 367)

20-14 Referring to Revelation 16:8,9, give a brief description of the fourth bowl judgment. (p. 367)

20-15 Referring to Revelation 16:10,11, what occurs in association with the fifth bowl judgment? (p. 367)

20-16 Why will not men repent as a result of the fifth bowl judgment? (p. 367)

20-17 Looking at Revelation 16:12-14, 16, what will be the sixth bowl judgment? (p. 367)

THE SEVENTH BOWL JUDGMENT

20-18 According to Revelation 16:17-21, how severe will the seventh bowl judgment be, and describe the effects of this final bowl judgment? (pp. 369-370)

20-19 According to Revelation 16:19, what two cities are specifically mentioned as being destroyed — along with all the other cities of the world — and what are they? (p. 370)

20-20 With many of the mountains of the world being leveled by the final bowl judgment, what might we assume, therefore, will happen to Mount Zion upon which the city of Jerusalem sits? (pp. 370)

THE MARRIAGE OF THE LAMB

20-21 According to Revelation 19:6b-8, what great event takes place in heaven while the final wrath of God is being meted out upon earth by His angels (His reapers)? (p. 371)

20-22 Who will comprise the bride that will be married to the Lamb? (p. 372)

20-23 What are some of the Old and New Testament passages that tie the Old and New Testament believers together as the bride of Christ? (pp. 372-373)

20-24 What does the heavenly city mentioned in Hebrews 11:16 and John 14:2,3 refer to in particular? (p. 373)

20-25 Does Scripture ever refer to two heavenly cities and two brides of Christ, or only one? (p. 373)

THE FINAL SHOWDOWN

20-26 At the end of the thirty-day reclamation period, what is the final event that culminates the wrath of God, according to Revelation 19:11-16? (p. 374)

20-27 Why must the armies that accompany Christ to earth at the battle of Armageddon be His angels rather than His bride? (pp. 374-375, 517 endnote 4)

THE BATTLE OF ARMAGEDDON

20-28 What two Old Testament passages give a parallel account of Armageddon (p. 376)

20-29 What two passages from Daniel give a vivid portrayal of Antichrist's eternal end? (p. 377)

20-30 What clear sequence of events concerning end-times do we find after a close examination of these two passages in Daniel? (p. 377)

FINAL DESTINATION OF THE BEAST AND HIS PROPHET

20-31 According to Revelation 19:20, what is the final destiny of Antichrist and his false prophet? (p. 378)

20-32 What is the discrepancy between Revelation 19:20 and Ezekiel 39:11 as it concerns the ultimate destruction of Antichrist? (p. 378)

20-33 Are there any other biblical passages that confirm Ezekiel's position that Antichrist is killed at the battle of Armageddon? (p. 378)

20-34 How does Isaiah 14:12-20 help to clear up this seeming problem? (p. 379)

FINAL DISPOSITION OF MAGOG

20-35 According to Ezekiel 39:4-6, what happens to the nation of Magog, and why? (pp. 379-380)

EDOM BECOMES A MEMORIAL

20-36 According to Isaiah 34:1,2, 4,5, 8,10, what will happen to Edom as a result of the day of the Lord, and why? (pp. 380-382)

20-37 According to Obadiah 15, God forewarned Edom with what event, should Edom sin against Israel in the "day of their [Israel's] disaster"? (p. 381)

CHAPTER
TWENTY-ONE

THE RESTORATION PERIOD

F **CHAPTER FOCUS:**

In this chapter you will study the events that occur during the Restoration Period — the 45 days immediately preceding the Millennium. First will come the restoration of God's holy mountain, Mount Zion, with the restoration of the millennial Temple on its summit, then the restoration of the remnant of Israel back to the holy mountain of God, and finally, the last event of the restoration period which will be by far the most important.

R **Read chapter 21 of _The Sign_ before answering the following questions.**

WHAT IS THE RESTORATION PERIOD?

21-1 According to Daniel 12:11,12, how long will the restoration period be and when will it occur in relationship to the Millennium? (p. 384)

....

....

....

WHAT THINGS WILL HAPPEN?

21-2 What three magnificent events will happen during the restoration period? (pp. 384-385)

   1. ....

....

2. ....

....

3. ....

21-3 The restoration period will be the time of what other two significant events? (p. 385)

1. ....

2. ....

THE RESTORATION OF MOUNT ZION

21-4 When, according to Revelation 16:19-20, was Mount Zion destroyed? (p 385)

....

....

21-5 According to Revelation 19:20, how should "the mountains were not found" be better translated, and what significance does this have regarding other Old Testament prophecy (Ezekiel 39:4)? (pp. 385-386)

....

....

....

21-6 According to Zechariah 14:10 when compared to Revelation 16:19-20, what one place will have all the mountains leveled during the seventh bowl judgment?

....

....

21-7 How does Zechariah, the Old Testament prophet, specifically describe the seventh bowl judgment of Mount Zion in the first half of verse 10, chapter 14? (p. 386)

....

21-8 According to Isaiah 2:2, what must occur to Mount Zion before the Millennium begins? (p. 386)

21-9 According to Ezekiel 40:2, how does Ezekiel refer to this new Mount Zion? (p. 386)

THE RESTORATION OF ISRAEL

21-10 According to Jeremiah 31:10-12a, what is significant about Israel's return to her land? (p. 386)

21-11 According to Jeremiah 31:12a, when Israel returns to the land in belief, where specifically do they come to? (p. 387)

21-12 Where will this believing remnant of Israel returning to Mount Zion come from primarily? (p. 387)

GENTILE NATIONS TO MOUNT ZION

21-13 According to Isaiah 66:16, 18,19, who else will come to Mount Zion during the forty-five-day period that immediately precedes the Millennium? (p. 389)

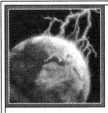

THE RESTORATION OF THE TEMPLE

21-14 According to Ezekiel 42:1, 7, what will be the last event to be completed <u>on earth</u> by Christ during the forty-five-day period immediately preceding the Millennium? (p. 390)

21-15 According to Zechariah 6:13, what will be the purpose of the millennial Temple? (p. 390)

21-16 According to Zechariah 6:12,13, who will build the millennial Temple? (p. 391)

THE LAYOUT OF MOUNT ZION

21-17 What four important things do we learn from Old Testament prophecy concerning the lay of the land on top of the new, elevated Mount Zion? (p. 392)

1.

2.

3.

4.

21-18 Who does Ezekiel 37:24,25 identify as "the prince," the man who shall reign directly over Israel under Christ during the millennial kingdom? (p. 392)

RESTORING THE RULE UPON EARTH

21-19 According to Daniel 7:27, what will be the most important event of the restoration period that occurs in heaven sometime during the forty-five-day restoration period? (p. 392)

21-20 We know that God Almighty reclaims the rule over earth before the final wrath of God (Revelation 11: 15-18) but according to Daniel 7:11-14, when is Christ given dominion over His kingdom, before or after Antichrist is slain? (p. 393)

21-21 Therefore, as Antichrist is killed at the end of the thirty days that follow the seventieth week (see Daniel 12:11), and as Christ will physically rule over the millennial kingdom forty-five days later, Christ must receive His kingdom during what specific time frame? (p. 392)

21-22 According to Daniel 7:27, how permanent will Christ's reign be? (p. 394)

Personal Notes & Quotes:

TWENTY-TWO

THE MILLENNIUM BEGINS

F **CHAPTER FOCUS:**

In this final study you will carefully examine the events that transpire on the first day of the Millennium. There are five critical events that occur, and it is important that the student of prophecy not only understand what these events are, but clearly be able to explain why they must occur in the order that they do. Much confusion arises, for example, to those who wish to put the new heavens and earth after the Millennium rather than before, where biblically it must occur. Therefore, the sequence of these events that occur on the first day of the Millennium, as well as the biblical logic behind the order of events explained in this chapter, are very important and should, therefore, be understood by any serious student of biblical prophecy.

R **Read chapter 22 of *The Sign* before answering the following questions.**

22-1 What does the word "Millennium" in the prophetic sense refer to? (p. 395)

22-2 According to Revelation 22:1-5 cf. Isaiah 11:1-9, what could the earthly conditions be likened unto during the Millennial reign of Christ? (p. 396)

THE MILLENNIAL RULE OF CHRIST

22-3 What does the phrase found in Daniel 2:44, "this kingdom which shall endure forever" refer to? (p. 397)

22-4 According to Ezekiel 34:23,24, what will be the governing chain of command in the Millennial kingdom? (p. 398)

22-5 According to Revelation 21:24, who will directly rule over the Gentile nations that exist during the Millennium? (p. 399)

22-6 According to Isaiah 49:22,23, what will be the other nations' attitude toward Israel? (p. 300)

THE FIRST DAY OF THE MILLENNIUM

22-7 According to Revelation 20:1-4; 21:1,2, what are the five important events that will occur on the first day of the Millennium? (p. 400)

1.

2.

3.

4.

5.

FIRST EVENT: SATAN BOUND

22-8 According to Revelation 20:1,2, where is Satan during the Millennium? (p. 401)

SECOND EVENT: THE SHEEP AND GOATS JUDGMENT

22-9 According to Matthew 25:31-40, how are the true citizens of the kingdom of darkness, those who survive the day of the Lord, separated from the true citizens of the kingdom of God before entering the millennial kingdom of Christ? (p. 402)

22-10 Who conducts the Sheep and Goat Judgment? (p. 402)

22-11 According to Matthew 25:31, who will accompany the Lord at the Sheep and Goat Judgment. (p. 402)

22-12 According to Matthew 25:32, who will undergo the judgment of Christ at the Sheep and Goat Judgment? (p. 402)

22-13 With regards to the Greek word *ethnos*, translated "nations" or "peoples," does this term include people of Jewish ancestry? (p. 402)

22-14 In the opinion of the author, what two major considerations will be taken into account at the Sheep and Goat Judgment when the Gentile peoples will be judged? (p. 403)

1.

2. _____

_____

22-15 According to Isaiah 43:9-10 and 54:17, who will be the witnesses against these Gentile peoples at the Sheep and Goat Judgment? (p. 403)

_____

_____

_____

22-16 Will those Gentiles who helped Israel during the seventieth week be given salvation because of their works; in other words, will they be saved because they refused to worship Antichrist and helped Israel? (p. 404)

_____

_____

_____

22-17 How does Matthew 25:34 substantiate this truth? (p. 405)

_____

_____

THIRD EVENT: "BEHEADED" MARTYRS RESURRECTED

22-18 Who are the beheaded martyrs who will be given their resurrection bodies at this specific time, on the first day of the Millennium? (p. 406)

_____

_____

_____

CHAPTER 22 TWENTY-TWO

22-19 Is it possible that the resurrection of the beheaded martyrs in Revelation 20:4 could be referring to an earlier resurrection, prior to the first day of the Millennium? (pp. 518-519 endnote 4)

22-20 What does the first resurrection mentioned in Revelation 20:5 specifically refer to? (p. 405)

22-21 According to John 5:29 and Revelation 20:6, 14, what is the second resurrection? (pp. 405-406)

22-22 Technically, what are the four phases of the first resurrection? (p. 406)

1.

2.

3.

4.

Note: The author believes that Revelation 20:7-14 is merely a parenthesis explaining the "second death" introduced in the preceding verse, and referred to again at the end of verse 14, where it will occur for all unbelievers at the Great White Throne at the end of the Millennium.

FOURTH EVENT: NEW HEAVENS AND NEW EARTH

22-23 The next major event on the first day of the Millennium will be the renovation of the existing heavens and earth. According to 2 Peter 3:10 as well as many other passages in both the Old and New Testaments, why will a new heaven and a new earth be necessary at the beginning of the millennial rule of Christ? (p. 407)

22-24 What is the Old Testament proof that the "new heavens" and the "new earth" will be accomplished before the Millennium begins? (pp. 407, 519 endnote 6)

22-25 When referring to "new" heavens and earth, what does the term "new" really mean in the Greek? (pp. 407, 519 endnote 5)

FIFTH EVENT: THE NEW JERUSALEM

22-26 The final major event that will occur on the first day of the Millennium will be the descent of the New Jerusalem to earth from Heaven. According to Revelation 21:1-7 and John 14:2, what exactly is the New Jerusalem? (p. 409)

CHAPTER 22
TWENTY-TWO

22-27 What three important truths concerning the New Jerusalem do we find in Revelation 21:1-7? (pp. 409-411)

1.

2.

3.

22-28 According to Revelation 21:22, what is obviously missing in the New Jerusalem as it descends from heaven to earth? (p. 410)

22-29 Comparing Ezekiel 43:12 with 45:2,3, where will the temple of God be located during the Millennium?

22-30 Taking into consideration the previous three questions, where will the newly built Temple on the summit of Mount Zion be located in relationship to the New Jerusalem? (p. 410)

22-31 What will be the focal point of the New Jerusalem as well as the entire earth? (pp. 410-411)

22-32 Why, according to 1 Thessalonians 4:17 and John 14:2,3, must the New Jerusalem descend down to earth before the Millennial rule of Christ? (p. 410)

THE MARRIAGE SUPPER OF THE LAMB

22-33 When the bride of Christ is reunited with her Husband in the New Jerusalem on the first day of the Millennium (see Revelation 21:2, 9-10), what is the last great event given on earth in celebration of their recent wedding in heaven? (p. 411)

22-34 Who will be those who come to the marriage supper? (p. 412)

HOW WILL WE RESPOND?

22-35 According to Revelation 21:7, who will inherit all these marvelous things described in the final two chapters of Revelation?   (p. 413)

22-36 Write in your own words the life we should therefore live out of gratitude for what Christ has done for us from the foundations of the world and out of expectancy over what Christ will do for us in the last days as we approach the end of the age!

CHAPTER 1
FOUNDATIONS FOR UNDERSTANDING PROPHETIC TRUTH

1-1

1. Will the church go through the great tribulation?
2. When, in the sequence of end-time events, will the Rapture actually occur?
3. When does the wrath of God begin? Does it extend through the entire "seventieth week" or is it confined only to the final battle of Armageddon?

1-2

Most agree that the true church will be removed (raptured) before the wrath of God because God has promised to deliver the true church from His wrath.

1-3

Scripture is clear that believers are not promised freedom from persecution and tribulation but that they can, in fact, expect persecution and tribulation to come for the very reason that they are Christians (John 15:18,19; 1 Thessalonians 3:3,4; 2 Thessalonians 1:7; 2 Timothy 3:1, 12; 1 Peter 4:12,13; cf. vv. 3-7).

1-4

Believers will not undergo God's wrath but are not promised exclusion from the wrath of the world and of Satan, especially from the persecution of God's elect during the great tribulation by Antichrist.

1-5

1. All Scripture is to be taken in its customary, natural and normal sense (i.e. literal) allowing, of course, for obvious symbolism and figures of speech.
2. All Scripture must be taken within the context of a word, phrase, or larger passage.
3. Always compare Scripture with Scripture.
4. Antinomies are never acceptable.
5. Some prophetic passages of Scripture, in both Testaments, have both near and far implications and applications.

1-6

An antinomy is "a contradiction between two apparently equally valid principles or between inferences correctly drawn from such principles" (Webster's Ninth New Collegiate Dictionary).

1-7

Because comparison of the texts will sometimes reveal that the different terminology and styles of the writers are, in reality, describing the same event or issue with equal and consistent truthfulness, though often not in the same words, with the same detail or from the same perspective.

1-8

Our understanding of the end times will continue to increase as history continues to unfold and verify biblical prophecy. History has been, and will continue to be, a source of prophetic insight for those who carefully study God's Word.

1-9

It should go without saying that the Olivet Discourse (as recorded in Matthew 24-25) and the book of the Revelation are absolutely pivotal for understanding end-time events.

1-10

Both end-time passages are the direct teaching of Christ Himself.

1-11

The "seventieth week of Daniel" corresponds to the day of the Lord when God executes His wrath upon the earth, and therefore, the Rapture must occur before the beginning of this critical seven year period. Thus, this Rapture position is referred to as "pretribulational," with the entire seventieth week being designated as the "tribulation period," or the time of God's wrath.

1-12

No!

1-13

The origin of the "pretribulational" position is relatively new, dating back only to about 1830. Some, like John Walvoord in his book "The Rapture Question," attribute the position to John Darby and his associates. There is an equal number of scholars who give Edward Irving (considered the father of modern-day Pentecostalism) credit for originating this position. And some believe it originated from a fifteen-year-old girl named Margaret MacDonald through a vision.

1-14

The system known as amillennialism allegorizes prophetic Scripture, holding that there will be no physical, earthly millennial kingdom over which Christ will rule. The second coming of Christ is for the purpose of ending human history, at which time eternity future will immediately begin. They see no future, literal, personal Antichrist who will seek to destroy the elect of God in the last days, or a rapture of the church before the outpouring of God's wrath.

1-15

Simply stated, the prewrath view contends that the church will go through the great tribulation by Antichrist during the end times, but will be raptured before the wrath of God when Christ cuts short the persecution of Antichrist.

1-16

The position of all the early church fathers before the Council of Nicea in A.D. 325, with only two exceptions, was that the church would undergo the persecution of Antichrist during the great tribulation before the return of Christ, from which such persecution He would rescue His elect at His coming.

1-17

Such great church fathers as Clement of Rome, Barnabas, Justin Martyr, the Pastor of Hermas, Irenaeus, Hippolytus, Melito of Sardis, Methodius, Tertullian, Syrian, Commodianus, Victorinus and Lactantius stated clearly in their writings that the church would undergo the persecution of Antichrist before they were raptured.

1-18

The persecution of the church by Antichrist was clearly the position of the early church. Roman Catholicism under Augustine, heavily influenced by Origen, then moved away from the literal interpretation of end-time events and allegorized prophetic Scripture.

1-19

Since Christ's ascension back to Heaven as recorded in Acts 1, no prophetic event needs to be fulfilled before Christ's second coming. In other words, He could come at "any moment." This position is the critical cornerstone of pretribulationism.

1-20

No. We may fairly conclude that both pretribulationists and others who find imminence in the Ante-Nicene fathers are grasping at straws. The early church fathers uniformly expected a yet future persecution of Antichrist prior to the Lord's return.

1-21

One's view of the end times will have exceeding importance for believers who must suffer or be in real danger of the worst human oppression of all time. Christians will need to know the full truth of those times if they are to remain faithful to their Lord and confident in His Word.

1-22

The purpose of this book is to acquaint readers with the biblical sequence and importance of the many events that will occur during the end times.

1-23

It is the author's desire that the truths this book presents will be used of God to encourage and strengthen His children for personal faithfulness and holiness; for witnessing to the lost, especially lost Jews; and for steadfastness in sound doctrinal teaching, especially in the areas of prophecy concerning the last days.

1-24

No. To the faithful believer Christ is not coming like a "thief in the night," but "we are not of night nor of darkness; so then let us not sleep as other do, but let us be alert and sober."

CHAPTER 2
A WARNING TO THE CHURCH

2-1

The degree to which Christians will be persecuted by Antichrist and his ungodly forces in the last days (especially during the great tribulation) will be directly dependent on the degree to which we are spiritually prepared.

2-2

From beginning to end, this prophetic book is all about the return of Christ.

2-3

Although the Apostle John penned it, the instruction found in the book of Revelation is that of Jesus Christ.

2-4

The book of Revelation is directed to "the churches" - not only to the seven churches in Asia Minor of John's day, but also to all churches throughout the world who will encounter the Satanically inspired and empowered trials and afflictions of the end times.

2-5

These seven letters exemplify perfectly the near/far type of prophecies explained in chapter 1 of this book, common to prophetic passages found in both the Old and New Testaments. The seven churches do not represent stages in church history, but rather depict historical New Testament churches that exemplify various characteristics found in churches during all periods of church history and, as the language clearly states, will particularly characterize the condition of the church in the final days.

2-6

1. The faithful church (Philadelphia).
2. The dead church (Sardis).
3. The compromising church (Thyatira).
Note: It should be noted that references to dead, faithful and compromising churches are references to not only the church itself, but also to the individuals who comprise the church in general. In other words, a faithful church will be made up primarily of faithful Christians but may also include both dead and compromising individuals that attend as well. This is an important principle to remember as one works through out this teaching manual.

2-7

"Because you have kept the word of My perseverance, I also will keep you from the hour of testing, that hour which is about to come upon the whole world, to test those who dwell on the earth."

2-8

No.

2-9

The Greek verb, *tereo* that is translated "keep" in Revelation 3:10, best carries the basic idea of "protection within a sphere of danger."

2-10

The preposition *ek* is translated "from." The basic meaning of *ek* is "out from within" and best carries the idea of "deliverance from," rather than the simple idea of "keeping from." The translation "from" gives the reader the false idea of an external preservation from, rather than a deliverance "out from within," an existing condition that the object or subject of the sentence is in the midst of.

2-11

God's protection while "within a sphere of great danger" (i.e., during the great tribulation of Antichrist) with the promise of eventual removal out from within that dangerous time.

2-12

John 17:15. In its context Christ is praying for the "protection of" the believer while he is still in the world, the "sphere of danger" over which Satan rules, until the believer is safely "delivered out from within" this sphere of danger by death or rapture.

2-13

Most agree that "the hour of testing" can only refer to the great tribulation.

2-14

The Greek noun *peirasmos* carries the basic idea of "putting to a proof."

2-15

It is a direct reference to the "great tribulation" of Antichrist that occurs in the last days.

2-16

In both cases, the believer is present during the *peirasmos*, not kept away or outside of it while it is happening. This of course substantiates the proper translation of *tereo ek*, used in our critical passage, Revelation 3:10.

2-17

God promises faithful churches (genuine Christians) His protection while they are within a "sphere of great danger" (during the great tribulation of Antichrist), and the eventual removal "out from within" that dangerous time.

2-18

1. We see that the faithful church will persevere, will keep Christ's Word, and will not deny the name of Christ - in other words, she does not take the mark of the beast or worship his image.
2. Because of her faithfulness, she will receive the Lord's gracious promise that He will keep and protect her while within this sphere of danger (that is, during the hour of testing, the great tribulation), and that He will eventually deliver her out from within this sphere of danger - when He returns to "cut short" those days of terrible distress, rapture the true church, and pour out His holy wrath upon the unrighteous.
3. Christ will give the faithful a crown and a place of great honor and intimate fellowship with God in His eternal kingdom.

2-19

Christ promises the church of Philadelphia that "I am coming quickly," clearly a reference to His 2nd coming.

2-20

The Sardis church is spiritually dead.

2-21

They are the tares (counterfeit believers) who will have been sown in among the wheat (true believers) and will exist side by side with the wheat in the kingdom of heaven upon earth (the church) until God's time of harvest.

2-22

The unbelieving members of (or represented by) the Sardis church will suffer the judgmental destruction of God's fury that will shortly follow, when God's "day of the Lord" wrath is unleashed upon the unbelieving world at His second coming.

2-23

1. The dead church will be totally oblivious to the consequences of worshipping Antichrist, or his image, and of taking his mark. Many will do so without hesitation, still thinking themselves to be "good Christians," conforming to the world for the sake of survival instead of trusting in Christ.
2. When God's wrath is poured out on the Satanic world kingdom ruled by Antichrist, it will come upon these unregenerate church members "like a thief in the night."

2-24

Not all of the church-goers who make up the "spiritually dead" church will take the mark of the Beast but will seek to escape the wrath of Antichrist by going into hiding with their believing friends. When Christ returns, these "spiritually dead" men and women will be working side by side with the genuine believers, only to be left behind at the Rapture.

2-25

The parable of the virgins (Matthew 25:1-13).

2-26

1 Thessalonians 5:2 and 2 Peter 3:10. Both are a reference to the coming of Christ and the day of the Lord judgment that will follow.

2-27

Christ once again refers to His "coming like a thief," a direct reference to His second coming.

2-28

This church is not spiritually dead, but it is less than spiritually faithful genuine believers who are alive in Christ but are not living in His will, those who best characterize the decaying church at large just before the end times begin.

2-29

False teachers in the church were corrupting the gospel and causing many true believers, Christ's "bond servants," to stray from right belief and right living.

2-30

The lesson being taught is that being a true Christian is not in itself a protection against false doctrine.

2-31

The true but unfaithful believers who have committed spiritual adultery by following those false teachers will suffer "great tribulation, unless they repent."

2-32

It is used only two other times, Matthew 24:21 and Revelation 7:14. In both cases the term is dealing with the great tribulation of the last days.

2-33

Jesus Christ. Remember, the book of Revelation is the revelation of Jesus Christ.

2-34

No!

2-35

In all three passages Christ was referring to exactly the same thing, the great tribulation of Antichrist that will occur in the last days.

2-36

The church in general will definitely still be on earth during the great tribulation of Antichrist.

2-37

They will experience this persecution because they will believe what they have been falsely taught, without testing the words of men against the Word of God. Before Christ terminates the affliction by Antichrist on the compromising, He will sovereignly and lovingly use the affliction to cleanse and purify those Christians.

2-38

Christ's message to the church at Thyatira gives them an unqualified promise to return to take them to Himself. Again, as with the church of Philadelphia and Sardis, a direct reference to His second coming.

2-39

Faithful churches (Christians) will be offered God's protection within a sphere of danger - that is protection during the great tribulation by Antichrist.

2-40

Those who are spiritually dead (false Christians), are told that if they do not repent and turn to Christ, they will lose all opportunity for salvation and will endure the full wrath of His day-of-the-Lord judgment, which will come on them like a "thief in the night."

2-41

Genuine but unfaithful believers who represent the compromising church are told that they will face the full brunt of the great tribulation by Antichrist as a testimony to all the churches, that Christ is the one and only true Lord who searches the hearts and minds of men, the one who rewards or punishes with perfect justice and righteousness as He permits the persecution by Antichrist to purify and prepare His bride to stand pure and blameless in the day of our Lord Jesus Christ.

2-42

Abraham was given the warning concerning the impending disaster on Sodom and Gomorrah for the sake of his family, a warning that was to encourage righteous living. For this reason, it is important for us, our children, and our grandchildren to likewise live righteously with a right view of end times always in focus. Christians are cautioned, over and over, to live godly lives, looking for the return of Christ. (See 2 Peter 3:11-14,17,18).

2-43

1. What we think about the end times is critically important. Paul warns believers concerning the end times to "let no one in any way deceive you" (2 Thessalonians 2:3).
2. To the degree to which the genuine Christian is prepared he will either have the protection of God during the great persecution by Antichrist, or will feel the full brunt of Antichrist's fury in his attempt to kill all who will not bow down to him. A believer's theology concerning the last days, therefore, is of immense importance, especially for those who will actually live during those last days.
3. We can indeed be prepared!

CHAPTER 3
THE COSMIC CONFLICT

3-1

The immense conflict between God and Satan began at the birth of human history when the great archangel Lucifer rebelled against his Creator and Lord. That cosmic conflict has continued unabated since that day.

3-2

This is not a contest because the Victor was determined in eternity past, long before the conflict began.

3-3

All good in the universe is the kingdom of God, and all evil in the universe is the kingdom of Satan.

3-4

Every spirit being, including man, belongs to one realm or the other. Those who belong to the realm of goodness (the kingdom of God) are those who are under willing submission to God. Those who belong to the realm of evil (the kingdom of Satan) are those who are under submission to Satan. This is true whether we are conscious of it or not.

3-5

Like all other created beings, Satan is finite and vulnerable. Evil is the only thing Satan can truly claim as his own; and that evil, vast and pernicious as it is, is circumscribed by divine limits - in degree, in extent, and in time. Satan's intelligence and power not only are from God but are restricted by God.

3-6

He was foolishly blinded with pride, and, not being omniscient, he believed that with the power he had received from the Creator he somehow could subdue the Creator. It was with that wicked design that the cosmic conflict began.

3-7

The supreme ambition of Satan was and is to usurp God's sovereignty over the earth, especially over man, who was made in God's image and given divine authority to rule the earth as God's steward.

3-8

When they chose to believe Satan's word above God's, they chose Satan's lordship above God's; and in that act of disobedience, by default, they lost their rulership over the earth and their spiritual relationship to God.

3-9

No. All the posterity of Adam and Eve were corrupted and alienated from God, and the entire world, as well, suffered curse and corruption because of their sin.

3-10

Death.

3-11

Death is not annihilation but "separation."

3-12

The first death was spiritual, which brought eternal, spiritual "separation" from God and the kingdom over which He rules. God expelled mankind from His divine realm of spiritual life and light (the kingdom of God) and cast them into the realm of Satan's spiritual death and darkness (the kingdom of Satan) with the ultimate destiny of the lake of fire.

3-13

The second death caused by Adam's sin was physical. It is the "separation" of man's physical body from his eternal soul which lives forever.

3-14

Satan succeeded in dethroning man from his rulership over the earth after which he arrogantly claimed that authority to himself. He therefore now reigns as ruler of this present world and age.

3-15

God made it clear to Satan how his defeat would come, telling him that a male descendant of the woman would bring his ultimate downfall and his destruction.

3-16

The first step was that God chose for Himself, His own kingdom of men and women over which He would rule, the "spiritual descendants" of Abraham. **Note:** Those He chose eventually become the citizens of the kingdom of God, each specifically at that point in life of their individual salvation.

3-17

Those who are the descendants of Abraham in the flesh. The Jewish race.

3-18

God's spiritual kingdom, His chosen spiritual line, was originally to come primarily from within the physical line of the nation of Israel that He established through Abraham, but because that nation continued in unbelief and disobedience, "salvation has come to the Gentiles, to make them [Israel] jealous" (Romans 11:11). Only after "the fullness of the Gentiles has come in . . . all Israel [the nation] will be saved" (vv. 25,26). When we speak of God's chosen people (the true citizens of the kingdom of God), then we speak of all who are the spiritual descendants of Abraham, both Jews and Gentiles - all who have received the divinely bestowed gift of faith and who through faith trust and obey Him.

3-19

The second step is that God chose Messiah (Christ) to redeem His chosen people (1 Peter 1:1,18-20), back from the kingdom of darkness, the domain of Satan, into the kingdom of God. The coming Messiah's first purpose was to pay the penalty of sin for those whom God chose in Christ "before the foundation of the world" (Ephesians 1:4).

3-20

The third step is that God chose the nation Israel (the natural line of Abraham) through which the Messiah and King (Christ) would come. To redeem a chosen remnant of mankind back to God from the kingdom of darkness, a price had to be paid to satisfy His holiness and justice, a price so immeasurably high that it could be satisfied only through the shedding of the blood of an absolutely pure and sinless sacrifice. God sovereignly ordained that this sacrifice (for the sin of the world) would come through the nation of Israel, fathered by Abraham and divinely protected on earth in order that the sacrificial-Messiah could not be cut off until He paid the necessary price for the redemption of the elect people of God's own choosing.

3-21

The fourth step is, God chose when He would destroy the kingdom of Satan, at a future time during the day of the Lord (Zephaniah 1:14-18).

3-22

The fifth step is that God chose when He would complete the spiritual kingdom of God, that is, when the entire nation of Israel that survives the final seven years of Gentile domination comes into a saving relationship with their true Messiah and King, Jesus Christ.

3-23

The sixth step is that God chose the precise time Christ (Messiah) would become King over all the earth (Daniel 7:11, 13, 14). When the seventh trumpet is blown, just after the completion of the seventieth week and the subsequent salvation of the natural line of Israel several days later, the reign over the earth will be reclaimed by God (Revelation 11:15). Several weeks later, after Antichrist and his armies are defeated by Christ and He has reclaimed the physical possession of earth, then the reign over earth will be given by the Ancient of Days to Christ.

3-24

Christ came as the Passover Lamb to permanently pay the price of sin - that price being the death of the perfect Lamb provided by God, paid through the shedding of Christ's blood at Calvary.

3-25

Christ came as the Passover Lamb to permanently overcome the effect of sin - that is, to set the citizens of the kingdom of God free from spiritual death, the eternal separation of man's soul from the presence of their God and King.

3-26

Christ came as the Passover Lamb to permanently redeem those chosen to be His people, the spiritual line of Abraham, back from the kingdom of darkness into the kingdom of God.

3-27

Christ's death and resurrection spelled the certain doom of Satan and his rule over earth.

3-28

Christ will first rescue the citizens of God's kingdom living upon earth when He appears before He systematically and thoroughly destroys the inhabitants of the kingdom of Satan in His day-of-the-Lord judgment.

3-29

Christ will destroy all the unrighteous (including the tares that fall away during their great hour of testing) during the day of the Lord (Zephaniah 1:18; Isaiah 13:11a).

3-30

Christ will reclaim for God the natural line of Abraham (Israel), completing the kingdom of God.

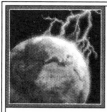

3-31

Christ will reclaim physical possession of the earth when He defeats Antichrist and his armies at the final battle of Armageddon (Revelation 19:11, 19-21; Zechariah 14:9).

3-32

Satan's first strategy was his attempt to destroy or disqualify the line of Messiah, the nation of Israel. As soon as he became aware of God's intentions, his counter-offensive was to try to disqualify by deception or to destroy by Gentile nations the nation of Israel, from whom the Redeemer and King would come. History, especially as found in the Old Testament, gives abundant evidence of Satan's success in his attempt to deceive the natural line of Israel. Likewise, the Old Testament also shows that Satan, unable to completely deceive God's chosen nation, has simultaneously attempted to carry out his parallel strategy of Israel's complete destruction by the hands of Gentile nations.

3-33

Satan did not totally succeed in deceiving Israel. God always had His remnant, the spiritual descendants of Abraham within the natural line of Abraham, who would obey Him. These survived.

3-34

Beast Empires. (See Glossary)

3-35

There are eight "beast empires" which Satan has used and will use in his attempt to eliminate the natural line of Israel.

3-36

Satan's second strategy was his attempt to destroy or disqualify Christ Himself.

3-37

No.

3-38

Satan, "ruler of the world" (John 16:11), offered to give Christ rule over the earth without His having to pay the awful redemption price of the cross - the specific purpose for which Christ had come to earth. Had Christ succumbed to that temptation, He would have disqualified Himself as Redeemer of the spiritual descendants of Abraham, the elect citizens of the kingdom of God.

3-39

Satan's final strategy will be to rekindle and redouble his efforts to kill any citizen or potential citizen of the spiritual kingdom of God, especially from within the nation of Israel.

3-40

Michael the archangel.

3-41

"The woman." The primary target of Satan's fury will again be an obedient remnant of Israel (from the natural line of Abraham, not the spiritual line), whose salvation, as a nation in its entirety, will complete the spiritual kingdom of God just before He reclaims the absolute reign over the earth from Satan.

3-42

His secondary target will be the "rest of her offspring, who keep the commandments of God and hold to the testimony of Jesus" (Revelation 12:17; 13:7, 8).

3-43

Any true believer chosen of God - Jew or Gentile - the church. In reality, all of the spiritual descendants of Abraham alive during the last days.

3-44

Saints!

3-45

The final conflict is played out in the last days. Michael and his holy angels will cast Satan and his demonic angels out of Heaven and down to earth (Revelation 12:7-9), purifying the heavens and setting the stage for this final conflict. God long ago ordained that His Son, Jesus Christ, would be both Redeemer and King, the eternal Victor in the cosmic conflict. Therefore, the final outcome has never been in doubt.

CHAPTER 4
THE BLESSINGS AND THE CURSES

4-1

The law was a reflection of God's own holy and righteous nature, and its purpose was to guide His people into lives of moral and spiritual holiness and uprightness, to preserve the line in which their Redeemer and King would eventually come, and to protect them from the ungodly influences of a hostile world that was under Satan's control.

4-2

We see God's gracious promise of blessing for walking in obedience.

4-3

Curses. First there would be natural affliction (Leviticus 26:16), then human affliction (v. 17), and then divine affliction (vv. 18-19). After that would come futility in their work (v. 20), decimation of their families and flocks (vv. 21-22), and execution by their enemies (v. 25). If the statutes of God were still rejected, God would turn Jew against Jew (vv. 28-29), destroy Israel's Temple and cities (vv. 30-32), and ultimately scatter her among the nations where she would perish (vv. 33, 38, 39).

4-4

God would ultimately scatter Israel among the nations where she would perish.

4-5

Yes.

4-6

God determined He would always have an obedient remnant from within the natural line of Abraham — as He would also from the church in general — the spiritual descendants of Abraham. These spiritual descendants of Abraham would be the citizens of the kingdom of God, men and women who would be obedient to their God and King.

4-7

Her disobedience became progressively worse.

4-8

The scattering of the nation.

4-9

This final curse would occur after their Messiah had come fulfilling God's promises to provide the true citizens of God's kingdom, a Redeemer through the seed of Abraham, and only after Israel's rejection of their Messiah and King. This ultimate curse found its literal fulfillment in A.D. 70 when the human armies under General Titus utterly destroyed Israel because of the Jews' persistent rebellion against Rome.

4-10

"Strike the Shepherd that the sheep may be scattered."

4-11

The Great Diaspora.

4-12

1. The Jews will return to the land that their forefathers possessed (Deuteronomy 30:5). But because they will return, still in unbelief, they will not recognize God's sovereign provision of that blessing, but will rather consider it to be their own achievement.
2. The nation of Israel will be brought into right relationship with her Messiah and King, completing the citizenship of the spiritual kingdom of God.
3. Israel's enemies will forever be destroyed, putting an end to the kingdom of darkness.
4. God's specially chosen nation will forever obey and serve her Savior and Lord (v. 8) when Christ physically rules over the earth.

4-13

No one knows the day or the hour when Christ will return. But according to verses 32-33, we can be aware of the seasons and so are exhorted in verse 42 to be on the alert. Jesus' words ring with urgency to every generation, but have a special immediacy for us today — now that the Jews once again have control of the land of Israel.

CHAPTER 5
THE "SEVENTY WEEK" PROPHETIC TIMETABLE

5-1

The "seventy weeks" refer to seventy time periods of seven prophetic years each, or a total of 490 prophetic years.

5-2

360 days.

5-3

Your people and your holy city. The nation of Israel and the city of Jerusalem.

5-4

Israel and their holy city, Jerusalem, will have 490 more years of direct Gentile domination before (1) they will have atoned for their sin to God, and (2) before everlasting righteousness will be brought in to the nation.

5-5

The "Time of the Gentiles" and the "Fullness of the Gentiles."

5-6

It is speaking here of the salvation of the entire natural line of Abraham who survive the seventieth week of Daniel (the fullness of the Gentiles).

5-7

After "the fullness of the Gentiles has come in [at the completion of the 70th week when Israel's sin have been atoned for]. . . all Israel will be saved [everlasting righteousness will be brought in]."

5-8

Gabriel revealed to Daniel that there would be a period of sixty-nine seven-year periods (483 years) from the time a decree would be given to "restore and rebuild Jerusalem" until "Messiah the Prince" (Daniel 9:25). The decree referred to here was actually given in 445 B.C. by Artaxerxes Longimanus (See Nehemiah 2:5-8). In exact fulfillment of this prophecy, the time between the decree and coming of Christ to Jerusalem, on Palm Sunday, has been calculated as being exactly 483 prophetic years of 360 days each.
Note: This is an important prophecy to understand and an incredible argument to use when dealing with unsaved Jewish friends concerning the Messiahship of Jesus Christ.

5-9

It provides a step-by-step outline of God's prophetic timetable.

5-10

The first 483 years of Daniel's prophecy are now past. We are in the gap between the sixty-ninth and seventieth week, with the final 7 year period still being future.

5-11

In this passage we find the last half of the seven years (along with the brief seventy-five day period of time that follows the end of the seven years until the Millennium begins) outlined in terms of days. In particular, we know this because the phrase "from the time the regular sacrifice is abolished" which occurs at the midpoint of the final week (see Daniel 9:27).

5-12

There is an additional interval of seventy-five days (comprised of two time periods, one of thirty days and the second of forty-five days), both of which transpire after the completion of the seventieth week but before the Millennium begins.

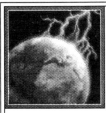

5-13

First, Messiah will be "cut off." The crucifixion of Christ. Second, the people of the prince will destroy the city and the sanctuary, referring to the destruction of Jerusalem and the Temple, initiating the Diaspora of Israel.

5-14

Christ was killed only several days after Palm Sunday, and the destruction of the city and the Temple occurred in A.D. 70.

5-15

The seventieth week of Daniel is initiated with a covenant that will be made with "the many." In context, "the many" is the nation of Israel. The completion of the seventieth week will "bring in everlasting righteousness," or in other words, the salvation of Israel.

5-16

No.

5-17

The "gap."

5-18

Because Israel rejected her Redeemer and King, Jesus Christ, God extended His Kingdom to the Gentiles to make the nation of Israel jealous.

5-19

God has promised that when "the fullness of the Gentiles has come in; . . . all Israel will be saved."

5-20

At the end of the seventieth week.

5-21

The interlude between the sixty-ninth and seventieth weeks has brought in salvation for the Gentiles, in order to make the nation of Israel jealous because of her rejection of her true Messiah and King.

5-22

Satan must do all in his power to prevent what God has clearly predicted He will do with Israel - namely, bring the entire nation back to Himself in salvation, completing the spiritual kingdom of God and spelling certain doom to Satan and his kingdom of darkness.

5-23

It will be during the seventieth week (the last seven years of the times of the Gentiles) that Satan will make that last great effort to preserve his domination over the earth.

5-24

Because of Israel's recent return to and rule over her own homeland (including the entire city of Jerusalem), the present generation of the church is the first since the early church before the Diaspora of A.D. 70 that can look with well-founded expectation for the events that will initiate the seventieth week.

5-25

Antichrist must first establish his eighth beast empire, or at least its three-nation power base that will drive the final beast empire of Satan. Such a formation could be assembled almost overnight. And when it is, the stage will be set for Israel to make a covenant (Daniel 9:27) with the powerful ruler of that empire.

CHAPTER 6
THE FIRST SEVEN BEAST EMPIRES

6-1

Beasts. Thus, for this reason, the author labels the different empires that have been used by Satan throughout history, "beast empires."

6-2

Satan's "beast empires" are at the center of his counter-strategy in the cosmic conflict between God and Satan as it is being waged here on earth.

6-3

The first seven empires and their leaders.

6-4

The "ten horns" represent the ten kings who will comprise the eighth beast empire.

6-5

The eighth empire comprising the ten horns will be ruled by one of the prior seven heads (or kings) of one of the previous seven beast empires who will come back to life to rule over the final beast empire. The ten kings who arise and receive authority with the beast (Antichrist) will comprise that eighth and final beast empire.

6-6

In this passage God's divinely revealed interpretation omits the first two empires mentioned in Revelation, focusing instead only on those empires which would dominate Israel and her holy city, Jerusalem, from Daniel's to the very last beast empire that will dominate Israel and Jerusalem during the seventieth week. Therefore, the beast empires represented in Nebuchadnezzar's dream are the third, fourth, fifth, sixth and "last" beast empires of Satan.

6-7

The Medo-Persian empire.

6-8

1. The lion is the same as the gold empire.
2. The bear is the same as the silver.
3. The leopard is the same as the bronze.
4. The fourth beast with ten horns becomes the final beast empire led by the little horn, which again corresponds directly to the fourth empire of Nebuchadnezzar's statue (legs of iron) that extends down to the final empire (ten toes of iron mixed with clay).

6-9

The accurate identification of these first six empires is helpful in our understanding of the seventh empire and our identification of Satan's final empire in the last days.

6-10

The biblical descriptions of the people that will comprise the final beast empire leave no doubt about their ancestry (even if there may be some uncertainty about their exact geographic location today).

6-11

Their hatred and subjugation of the Hebrew people.

6-12

1. Egyptian (Hamitic).
2. Assyrian (Semitic).
3. Babylonian (probably Semitic).
4. Medo-Persian (Japhetic).
5. Greek (Japhetic).
6. Roman (Japhetic).

6-13

During the first 69 weeks (483 years) of Daniel's seventy-week "curse" on Israel, all of the beast empires that Satan has used have come from the same ancestral background - namely, Japhetic.

6-14

The seventh beast empire dominates the nation of Israel while she is dispersed from her homeland, *during the gap* between the 69th and 70th weeks. Daniel's prophecies concerning the empires, however, deal only with the beast empires that dominate the nation of Israel, while she has access to her own land and the city of Jerusalem, specifically du*ring the seventy weeks (490 years)*

6-15

This intervening gap came about as the result of Israel rejecting her Messiah, thereby delaying the last seven-year period. (compare Zechariah 13:7)

6-16

If Israel had not rejected her Messiah, the Great Diaspora would have never occurred and the seventieth "week" would have begun without the seventh beast empire ever coming into existence and the final beast empire would have come directly out of the Roman Empire. That is not to say that Christ would not still have died. For this was the very purpose of His first coming. But the seventieth week would have begun sometime shortly after Christ's death and resurrection, since the need to "graft in" the Gentiles to make "Israel jealous" would have been eliminated (See Romans 11:11-26).

6-17

After. The book of Revelation was written approximately 90 A.D., twenty years after the Diaspora had begun.

6-18

Unlike the others, it would brutalize the people of Israel during the intervening gap between the sixty-ninth and seventieth week - when Israel is out of her land, dispersed among the nations to the ends of the earth.

6.19

1. It must come after the sixth beast empire (Rome).
2. It must persecute the Jewish people while they are out of their land, dispersed "from one end of the earth to the other."
3. It "must remain a little while" (Revelation 17:10b).
4. It would be hideously cruel in its persecution and slaughter of the Jewish people as prophesied in the curses recorded in Deuteronomy (see 28:64-67).
5. It must exist and come to an end before Israel would return to her land.
6. Since Israel returned to her land as a nation in 1948, there is only one thing we can conclude - the seventh beast empire had to have existed sometime between A.D. 70 and 1948.

6-20

The shocking reality is that only one nation in history fits these criteria - Nazi Germany, the Third Reich, under the absolute and demonic dictatorship of Adolph Hitler!

6-21

The Germanic Empire created by Kaiser Bismarck in 1871.

6-22

The Holy Roman Empire**.**

6-23

The two overriding ambitions of Hitler were, first, to establish a thousand-year reign over the entire world - the counterfeit millennium of a demonic mes siah and, second, to totally exterminate all Jews.

6-24

This eighth empire will be the last and by far the worst. It will be a unique composite of the previous beast empires since the time of Daniel and will be driven primarily by the descendants of Japheth, properly called Aryans, who historically have been anti-Semitic in the extreme. It will also somehow be tied to the same ancestry that drove the Roman Empire (the iron legs), becoming the iron component of the toes of iron and clay, as depicted in Nebuchadnezzar's statue.

CHAPTER 7
THE EIGHTH AND FINAL BEAST EMPIRE

7-1

Although certain historical events, such as the restoration of Israel as a nation in 1948, have indisputable end-times significance, it is foolish and futile to attempt to relate all major contemporary events or circumstances to biblical prophecy - even when they profoundly involve Israel or other parts of the Middle East. And even when one starts with biblical revelation, identifying current events with specific biblical end-time events should be done with tentativeness and the utmost caution.

7-2

The significance of all three of these passages that describe the 8th beast empire is that the strength of the final beast empire, the iron, will somehow be connected to the ancestry of the 6th beast empire, coming from the "legs of iron" - in other words, from the ancestry of the Roman Empire. Therefore, before we can identify which nations will be part of Antichrist's final ten-nation confederacy, it is necessary to have at least some understanding of what the ancestry of Rome was.

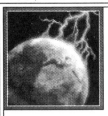

7-3

The Table of Nations tracks the ancestry of Noah after the flood through his three sons, Shem, Ham and Japheth, who are, therefore the fathers of all nations in the world today.

7-4

The Semitic peoples are considered Jewish or Arabic, the Hamitic peoples are black, and the Japhetic peoples are the fair-skinned Caucasian races.

7-5

After the flood God commanded Noah's family to "be fruitful and multiply and fill the earth." However, some three hundred years later they made plans to deliberately disobey God's command to disperse throughout the world by choosing to stay together in one location, to build a city (Babylon) and a tower (Babel) to reach upwards to God.

7-6

God declared that the name of that place (where they chose to remain in disobedience) would become Babel, because it was there that "the Lord confused the language of the whole earth; and from there the Lord scattered them abroad over the face of the whole earth."

7-7

The Japhetic tribes of Magog, Meshech, and Tubal are considered to have been especially nomadic.

7-8

They probably were among the first to push out the fringes of civilization, initially to the north. It was not by human determination but by divine decree that those particular people groups, as well as all others throughout history, eventually settled in the areas where they did.

7-9

The key issue is <u>ancestry, not geography</u>. It is also important to remember that, depending on whose ancestry is being tracked, some people moved a ways and then stayed there, some stayed in one particular area while their sons settled in new and different areas, and others kept moving and did not finally settle down until after much of the Old Testament was written.

7-10

Ten ancestral groups will combine with each other for the final campaign against God's chosen nation Israel, as well as the church in general during the last days, but they will still maintain their separate, ancestral identities under the absolute iron grip of leadership that traces its roots back to ancient Rome. Thus, it will be from the "iron" represented in the legs of iron in Nebuchadnezzar's statue that the leadership — the strength, so to speak — of the ten-nation eighth and final beast empire will arise.

7-11

No. The men who established the Roman Empire came to the Italian peninsula long after it had already been inhabited by the descendants of Kittim (another one of the sons of Japheth, but not the one from which Roman ancestry is derived).

7-12

Magog, Meshech or Tubal - although Magog seems most likely because it was these people who finally settled in the area (central Europe) from which the migration into the Italian peninsula originated.

7-13

Because Israel is presently firmly established back in her own land with possession of her holy city Jerusalem. The unification of those three nations is the only prophetic event that must yet occur before the seventieth week of Daniel can commence.

7-14

The passage itself declares explicitly that the events described in it will take place "in the latter years" (38:8) and "in the last days" (v. 16).

7-15

These two chapters describe in detail what has been introduced in the previous two chapters - that is, God's prophetic promise of a new covenant with Israel in the end times (chapter 36), and the initial return of Jews to the land of Israel in unbelief, depicted by the dry bones, after which again the national salvation of Israel is foretold (chapter 37).

7-16

The divine "wrath" in Ezekiel 38:19 translates the same Hebrew word ('ebrah, see Strong's #5678), used twice in Zephaniah 1:14-18, to describe the wrath that will characterize God's day-of-the-Lord judgment of the nations (vv. 15,18).

7-17

The events described in Ezekiel 38,39 have many parallels to passages in the book of Revelation that indisputably relate to the seventieth week.
(1) The birds of Ezekiel 39:17-20 correspond to the birds in Revelation 19:17,18, 21.
(2) Ezekiel's prediction that the Lord's final judgment against the ungodly nations who have persecuted Israel "shall be done" (39:7,8) corresponds to two passages in Revelation that speak of His final judgment of the nations, especially those of the eighth beast empire, as already having been accomplished, declaring proleptically but with absolute finality, "It is done" (16:17; 21:6).
(3) The final destruction of Gog and his armies described in Ezekiel 39:1-4 corresponds remarkably to the final destruction of Antichrist and his armies described in Revelation 19:17-21 and Isaiah's prophecy concerning the armies of Antichrist in the last days (Isaiah 34:1-3).

7-18

The ultimate salvation of the entire nation of Israel introduced earlier in both chapter 36 and 37 is portrayed in Ezekiel 39:21-29 as following the events previously outlined in chapters 38 and 39. This is in perfect harmony with Daniel 9:24, where we are told that "everlasting righteousness" will be brought in to Israel *after* the seventieth week is complete (cf. Romans 11:25-26). Nowhere in Scripture are we told that the nation of Israel in its entirety will be saved twice. Therefore, by the very fact that Israel's national salvation occurs exactly at this place in Ezekiel 38-39, we know that the preceding events must be among the same seventieth-week events described in the prophetic books of Daniel and Revelation, events which occur just before the national salvation of Israel.

7-19

The ultimate salvation of Israel depicted in Ezekiel 38-39 is immediately followed by the detailed prophecies of the millennial kingdom (chapters 40-48), when Christ will rule over a redeemed and obedient house of Israel. (See Charles Ryrie quote).

7-20

Gog was considered by many Jewish rabbis and by ancient Hebrew writings as the ungodly king who with arrogant futility will pit himself against Messiah in the end times. That concept perfectly fits the description of Antichrist given in the New Testament.

7-21

The wording suggests that Gog (who, as we shall see, must be Antichrist) is a Magogite and will rule over three nations, Rosh, Meshech, and Tubal — in perfect consistency with the critical prophetic passage in Daniel 7 that pictures the little horn over throwing the three larger horns (v. 8).

7-22

Rosh is not found in the table of nations, therefore is not biblically identified with any of the sons of Noah. On the other hand, *Rosh* is a title of leadership, and therefore, the reference to *Rosh* could be understood in this context rather than as nation.

7-23

Chief prince.

7-24

The ancestry of the three nations over which Antichrist will lead, initially, will be Magog, Meshech, and Tubal. In addition, Gog or Antichrist will come out of the ancestry of Magog.

7-25

The *Targum Jonathan* renders Magog as Germanic. Rabbi Samuel ben Ammi maintains that the sons of Japheth (Gomer, Magog, etc.) correspond to Africa, Germania, and Mysia. He goes on to say that Magog is Caucasia which was at one time inhabited by the Goths, which as we know are a Germanic people. It seems that the Germanic line as we know it today is descended from Magog. However, as clear as the ancestry of the Magogites may be, the exact geographical location is much less clear.

7-26

Certain Jewish writings indicate that by the eighth century A.D. the descendants of Meshech and Tubal were located in what is the western portions of the former U.S.S.R., with Meshech in the west near Moscow, and Tubal in the far western sections of Siberia near the city of Tobolsk, which is located in the former west central U.S.S.R., more than a thousand miles east of Moscow.

7-27

The logical conclusion is that the Magogites, from which the Germanic lineage descended, were the founders of the Roman Empire, which grew out of the city-state they had founded earlier. It is more than coincidental that the German title Kaiser is derived from Caesar and that so much of today's German culture can be traced directly back to the old Roman Empire.

7-28

Because if these identities are true, it is obvious that sometime before the seventieth week of Daniel begins, the U.S.S.R. must divide (which has already happened), and at least two of the resulting provinces, or states, must be ruled independently by at least two of the three horns that will be uprooted by the "little horn" (Antichrist) when he comes into power (Daniel 7:8).

7-29

The ancestry of all three nations that will form the power base of the final beast empire will be Japhetic and zealously anti-Semitic.

7-30

It will crush and put an end to "all" these kingdoms. This would refer to the gold kingdom, the silver, the bronze and the iron kingdoms.

7-31

Yes.

7-32

"The bronze, the silver and the gold" - that is, the Greeks (descendants of Javan), the Medes and Persians (descendants of Madai and Tiras), and the Babylonians (descendants of Arpachshad).

7-33

In the general vicinity of modern Iraq.

7-34

In the general vicinity of modern-day Iran.

7-35

Modern Greece.

7-36

We find total consistency in both passages to our basic premise. The first three beasts in Daniel correspond exactly to the composite beast that John saw in his vision on Patmos, both of which refer directly to the kingdoms of gold, silver, and bronze depicted in Nebuchadnezzar's dream.

7-37

If Magog (Rosh), Meshech, and Tubal are the three power-base nations of the ten-nation eighth beast empire, it seems reasonable to assume that the other four nations mentioned in this passage (Ethiopia, Put, Gomer, and Beth-togarmah) will also be member nations, representing the remaining kingdoms of Nebuchadnezzar's statue.

7-38

Ethiopia is descended from Cush, a son of Ham, and corresponds to modern Ethiopia and probably eastern Sudan in East Africa.

7-39

Put was another son of Ham and corresponds to modern Libya.

7-40

Gomer was a son of Japheth and corresponds generally, it is believed, to the Ukraine republic in the western portion of the former U.S.S.R.

7-41

Togarmah (Beth-togarmah, "Beth" in the Hebrew meaning "house of") was a grandson of Japheth and again corresponds in general to the republic of Armenia in the south-western portion of the former U.S.S.R. and perhaps the far eastern portion of Turkey and northwestern portion of Iran.

7-42

All seven sons and one grandson of Japheth will be directly represented in the final composition of the nations.

7-43

Egypt and Assyria will not be a part of the eighth and final beast empire of Satan. As we will be seen in chapters 19 and 21 of this book, God will still have a remnant within those two nations, both Jewish and Gentile, and for that reason those nations are not a part of Antichrist's ten-nation consortium.

7-44

The seven secondary nations will literally surround Israel, while the armies of the other three nations, which will be from the north, may already be in Jerusalem with their leader, Antichrist.

CHAPTER 8
ANTICHRIST AND HIS FORESHADOW

8-1

A little or small horn.

8-2

A small horn.

8-3

Antiochus Epiphanies, who conquered and ravaged Israel and the Temple during the second century B.C..

8-4

Under the guise of friendship and the promise of protection, both men make covenants with the nation Israel.

8-5

As in the days of Antiochus, many in Israel will again commit great apostasy after the signing of the covenant as they again seek to gain the favor of this powerful world leader, who is the Antichrist, yet to be "revealed."

8-6

After making their treaties with Israel, and while Israel lives under a false sense of security, both men seek to conquer Egypt and then return to ravage Israel and desecrate her Temple.

8-7

Both men proclaim themselves to be gods and demand worship from their subjects. Those Jews who refuse to worship these men, become (became) the primary target of his wrath.

8-8

Both tyrants have to contend with groups of Jews who refuse to worship or serve them and who foment considerable dissension and opposition from the rural areas surrounding the city of Jerusalem when they learn of the despots' true character and intentions regarding Israel.

8-9

The only two blowings of the "trumpet of God" are related to the defeat of these two men.

8-10

Hanukkah was initiated following the defeat of Antiochus and the cleansing of the Temple that had been defiled by him. This festival commemorates Israel's deliverance from that ungodly tyrant Antiochus, and celebrates the restoration of the Temple and the purification of its altar. It also looks forward to the eventual return of God's glory to the Temple. In a remarkable way this prefigures what will happen after the end of the "seventieth week," forty-five days after the defeat of Antiochus. For the redeemed nation of Israel will once again observe Hanukkah in a unique and resplendent way - this time in remembrance of the defeat of Antichrist, in celebration of the rebuilding of the Temple by Christ Himself, and in recognition of the permanent return of God's glory to the Temple.

8-11

Understanding the sequence of events during the reign of Antiochus will give considerable insight into the sequences of events that will occur in the days of Antichrist.

8-12

Twice - First in Zechariah 9:13-16 and secondly in 1 Thessalonians 4:16 (cf. 1 Corinthians 15:51-52).

8-13

In Zechariah 9:14, God blew the trumpet just before Israel was delivered from Antiochus, and the second time God will blow the trumpet is just before Christ delivers the church (see I Corinthians 15:51-52; 1 Thessalonians 4:16) and initiates His day-of-the-Lord wrath upon Antichrist (see 2 Thessalonians 2:8) and those who worship him.

8-14

Antichrist's strategy will be to offer the world a false savior (messiah), a false king, and a false kingdom - satanic counterfeits of God's true Savior (Messiah), true King, and true kingdom - knowing that those who do not serve Antichrist either are/or become potential citizens of the kingdom of God. And because Satan failed to kill or disqualify the rightful Savior and King of the earth, Jesus Christ, Satan's only remaining hope will be to destroy all/or potential citizens of the kingdom of God.

CHAPTER 9
THE STAGE IS SET

9-1

The return of Israel to her own land in 1948 and her more recent control over Jerusalem in 1967.

9-2

This could hardly be a more accurate description of the moral and spiritual condition of the world today.

9-3

A general decay in culture.

9-4

It is remarkable to see just how far our culture is willing to go in tolerating and condoning the most offensive material.

9-5

In the area of film, the moral and spiritual decay of our culture is equally pervasive. But the impact of film on people's minds and behavior goes far beyond popular music with its ability to create a total experience of sight and sound, of image and emotion. As with popular music, some of the most highly acclaimed movies in recent years are unimaginably perverse.

9-6

Contemporary art is often a vehicle for the most debased ideas imaginable. The spiritual and moral decay of culture today is dramatically captured in the distorted mirrors of contemporary art and the media.

9-7

The second condition which must exist before the final seventieth week can begin has to do with the general climate of thought that will prevail in the last days. According to the above mentioned Scripture — with their hearts set on self-love and their minds perverted by false teachers and demonic doctrines — the world will be prepared to receive Antichrist as their god and king.

9-8

Most New Age groups have a philosophical-religious orientation largely based on eastern mysticism. The New Age Movement in general cannot be ignored because many of its basic tenets and practices correspond to biblical teaching about the end times. Satan is the supreme deceiver and counterfeiter - and so the New Age Movement offers him a ready means in his grand strategy. Christians are looked upon as members of an inferior race. Read the quotes given on pages 153-154 and you will see the fact that New Age teaching is preparing New Age followers for what God says will definitely occur. The consensus of New Age teaching is that Antichrist and his world system is the system everyone must follow. What is new today is that New Age thinking is filtering into every area of modern culture and spreading so rapidly.

9-9

Evolution.

9-10

Scientific uniformitarianism is the belief that all physical laws and principles - as well as all psychological and sociological laws and principles after the appearance of man - have operated in exactly the same way throughout time. 2 Peter 3:4 refers to this thinking as "for ever since the fathers fell asleep, all continues just as it was from the beginning of creation."

9-11

This theory is the driving force behind modern evolutionism, and the only position taught in the world's leading scientific institutions today.

9-12

The force behind creation is God, not evolution (scientific uniformitarianism)!

9-13

Scientific uniformitarianism obviously leaves no room for supernatural intervention, especially intervention by God.

9-14

The general condition of the professing church at large will be characterized by pervasive heresy and compromise.

9-15

Because of moral decay in society at large, many who claim the name of Christ will choose to capitulate rather than suffer criticism and possible persecution for His name's sake. Many churches will not have the courage or commitment to maintain doctrinal purity.

9-16

Many local churches, denominational bodies, and parachurch organizations not only will condone but will even promote every sort of false teaching and practice imaginable. Likewise, the prophetic views of many will promote a false security in the church - giving a false assurance that the afflictions revealed in the book of Revelation either do not apply to them, having been taught that the church will be "raptured away" before that time or that those afflictions are simply allegorical or historical and should therefore be "spiritualized away". Much of the decline in commitment and doctrinal purity is already evident in the church today, even among those who claim to be evangelical and conservative.

9-17

To purify the compromising church so that "even though tested by fire, may be found to result in praise and glory and honor at the revelation of Jesus Christ" rather than "shrink away from Him in shame at His coming."

9-18

The "near" message to the seven churches was specifically addressed to the apostle John's contemporaries in the seven first-century churches and applied in every detail to them. But the future relevance of the "far" message becomes plainly evident when the context is studied. The theme of the book of Revelation is the second coming of Christ. The warnings given to the seven churches in chapters 2 and 3, although having a near-term application, are primarily given as a warning to the church going into the seventieth week.

9-19

Christ speaks to five of the seven churches with reference to His second coming.

9-20

As we have already studied in some detail earlier in this chapter, it is clear that the vast majority of latter-day churches (or more specifically, professing Christians) will be far from pure and holy. For the most part they will be weak, insipid, and compromising - with low moral standards and poor and even false doctrine, and without spiritual leadership.

9-21

Paul's phrase in 2 Timothy 4:3, 4, "will turn away their ears from the truth," is significant, especially in light of the admonition with which the book of Revelation begins, calling believers to "<u>hear</u> the words of the prophecy, and <u>heed</u> the things which are written in it; for the time is near" (1:3). This phrase "everyone who has an ear, let him hear what the Spirit says to the churches" is Christ's closing warning to all seven churches.

9-22

Because of the corrupt nature of the church at large in the last days, the church must of necessity go through the "fiery testing" in order to both separate the tares (the look-alikes) from the wheat, and then to cleanse the compromising bond-servants of Christ and prepare her for becoming the bride of Christ, just before the earth's wicked are destroyed by the day-of-the-Lord wrath.

9-23

Both passages speak of the same event, testing for "the proof of your faith" that comes before the rapture of the church.

9-24

Those within compromising churches will quickly show their true colors, and many will align themselves with Antichrist rather than face persecution for something they truly do not believe . . . And although it will bear the full brunt of Antichrist's fury, the true Christians within the compromising church will be delivered "from the wrath to come," "saved, yet so as through fire."

9-25

The spiritually dead church can expect only the wrath of God, along with the rest of the wicked world.

9-26

The faithful church will experience the special protection of God within the sphere of danger, "that hour which is about to come upon the whole world, to test those who dwell upon the earth."

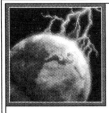

9-27

The Greek verb translated "overcome" in these verses is *nikao*, which comes from the Greek noun *nike* ("Victory" or "conquest"). An "overcomer" is one who never quits until complete victory is attained.

9-28

The real overcomer is the true child of God.

9-29

Unbelief — The fact that she would need purification of heart and cleansing from sinfulness indicates that she would not return in faith and righteousness.

9-30

Because the "everlasting righteousness" of the nation of Israel does not occur until after the seventieth week is complete, their return to the land must be in unbelief.

9-31

But the literal, historical nation of Israel is the absolute focal point of all end-time prophecy and therefore, to allegorize or spiritualize away the promises to Israel is to spiritualize away all end-time "events" — which of course, is exactly what many biblical interpreters have done through the centuries. Prophecy that need not be fulfilled literally is not prophecy at all, but mere "wishful thinking," especially as it pertains to the genuine church entering into the last days.

9-32

If the return of Israel to their homeland "cocked" the prophetic trigger in preparation for the end times, then her gaining control over the entire city of Jerusalem took off the "safety," preparing the weapon for firing.

9-33

Because the entire seventy week prophecy of Daniel deals with "your people [Israel] and your holy city [Jerusalem]." Therefore, the prophecies concerning the seventieth week could not be fulfilled until Israel had regained control of God's "holy city."

9-34

No, the rebuilding of the Temple on Mount Zion is not a prior condition to the beginning of the seventieth week. Because of the peculiar Greek word used for the end-time Temple, it is possible that an entire Temple will not be built, but only a tabernacle-like structure that could be erected quickly to provide a place for sacrifice. There are two Greek words translated Temple in the New Testament, *hieron*, which denotes the entire precinct of a place of worship and *naos* (used in 2 Thessalonians 2:4 and is our critical passage concerning the end times), which pertains only to the central sanctuary or holy place.

9-35

Before the seventieth week begins we can expect to see the overthrow and consolidation of those three nations to form the three-nation power base that Antichrist will use to build his empire. These three nations will become the power-base which he then will use to dominate the ten nation confederacy of Satan's final beast empire. Soon after this power-base confederacy is formed, its leader will initiate the seventieth week by making a "covenant of death" with Israel, who will despair in "sheer terror" (Isa. 28:15, 19) when the true identity of that leader is later revealed.

9-36

Close attention should be given to the events occurring in Germany and the former Soviet Union nations, since it is from some combination of these peoples that the "power-base three" will come.

CHAPTER 10
COUNTDOWN TO THE END OF THE AGE

10-1

Israel unwittingly will make a covenant with the powerful world leader (Antichrist incognito) thinking such a treaty will be her only hope for peace and security. Thus it will be the time of Israel's ultimate unfaithfulness.

10-2

The apostasy.

10-3

A "Covenant with death."

10-4

First the covenant with a pagan nation was made, and then the apostasy worsens as more and more Israelites forsake God's law and emulate the idolatry and immorality of their new ally. Israel's covenant with Antichrist will follow the exact same pattern.

10-5

We cannot be adamant as to whether or not Christians will know when this covenant is made, but as seen in the Epilogue, the author believes that the whole world will, in fact, know. Scripture gives no indication that it will be made in secret. Really, can Israel do anything today without making the headlines of practically every newspaper in the free world?

10-6

The nation of Israel will live in relative security because of the attractive but unholy alliance she has made with the most powerful world leader of that day.

10-7

A portion of Israel, most likely the majority in numbers, will willfully accept the covenant made with the Antichrist. But a small group of Jews, however, living in Israel at that time will know the truth and will use every opportunity to warn their fellow countrymen of their tragic mistake.

10-8

Seven.

10-9

All seven seals must be on the outside.

10-10

The seals must all be broken.

10-11

"The Lion from the tribe of Judah."

10-12

The Lamb, standing as if slain. Jesus Christ, who shed His blood for men from every tribe, tongue, people and nation.

10-13

This is a reference to Christ in His role as Judge rather than His role as Redeemer, which is captured in His title of "the Lamb."

10-14

The seven seals are the conditions that must be met *before* the scroll can be opened.

10-15

Always on the outside of the scroll

10-16

It has incredible significance when one realizes that at the breaking of the seventh seal, when the scroll is opened, the wrath of God (the day of the Lord) begins (Rev. 8:1-6).

10-17

Because God has determined that He "will judge the world in righteousness through a Man [Christ] whom He [the Father] has appointed, having furnished proof to all men by raising Him [Christ] from the dead."

10-18

Judgment. The wrath of God. The day of the Lord! And as we shall see in later chapters, that is exactly what happens when the seventh seal is broken and the large scroll is opened.

10-19

The judgment of the household of faith.

10-20

Compromise. "Holding to a form of godliness, although they have denied its power."

10-21

"The proof of your faith, having been tested by fire, may be found to result in praise and glory and honor at the revelation of Jesus Christ", or they will "shrink away from Him in shame at His coming."

10-22

God will use a "fiery ordeal" to come upon the church for it's testing, that fiery ordeal being the great tribulation of Antichrist which God will permit in order to search the minds and hearts of all who profess Christ, and gives to each one according to his deeds.

10-23

"The hour of testing, that hour which is about to come upon the whole world, to test those who dwell upon the earth."

10-24

They reside around the throne of God and have six wings.

10-25

First, they are seen praising God, saying "Holy, Holy, Holy, is the Lord of hosts . . . "
Secondly, they put the burning coal to the lips of Isaiah, purifying him before he comes into the presence of God.

10-26

The Seraphim.

10-27

They occupy an area in the center and around the throne of God, have six wings, and they are praising God, saying, "Holy, Holy, Holy, is the Lord God, the Almighty . . . "

10-28

The Seraphim.

10-29

The judgment of the household of faith . . . All of these events, then, will occur within the permissive will of God, overseen by the Seraphim who are responsible to identify and purify the true church from the professing church before they come into the presence of God Almighty, "that the proof of your faith, being more precious than gold which is perishable, even though tested by fire, may be found to result in praise and glory and honor at the revelation of Jesus Christ."

10-30

The Olivet Discourse as recorded in Matthew 24-25 and Luke 21:5-36. Mark 13 also records a portion of this discourse, but adds nothing to the accounts given in Matthew and Luke.

10-31

Because Christ is the author of both the Olivet Discourse and the book of Revelation. With the primary emphasis of both of these accounts being the end times, there should be — and there is — parallel teaching. One account defines the other, and visa versa.
Note: However, before we continue on with the opening of the individual seals, we must understand clearly why the four horsemen of Revelation 6 — that represent the first four seals — while permitted by God for the purification of the household of faith, definitely **cannot be** the wrath of God — the day of the Lord — as many churches, today, teach in an attempt to keep the church out of the seventieth week of Daniel.

10-32

Nowhere in Scripture are the first four seals of Revelation referred to as manifestations of His wrath during the day of the Lord.

10-33

God's wrath is not spoken of in Revelation until after the sixth seal is broken and the great cosmic disturbances are displayed as the sign of the end of the age.

10-34

Revelation 6:16,17. God's wrath is not spoken of in Revelation until after the sixth seal is broken and the great cosmic disturbances are displayed as the sign of the end of the age (see Matt. 24:3, 29). This sign (the sixth seal) then is the event which God has told His people will precede the day of the God's wrath (Joel 2:31). Thus after the sixth seal is broken we are told that "the wrath of the Lamb [Christ]" is about to commence (Revelation 6:15-17).

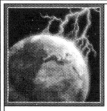

10-35

Christ associates the activities of the first seal with false christs (Matt. 24:5). If the four horsemen are instruments of God's wrath, then God would be in the unthinkable position of sending "false christs" as His own agents to deceive His own elect!

10-36

A house divided against itself cannot stand. That would certainly be the case if God was responsible for sending false christs to deceive His own elect.

10-37

If the entire seventieth week is the day of the Lord, the wrath of God would be *directly responsible* for the fifth-seal martyrdom of "the souls of those who had been slain because of the word of God, and because of the testimony which they had maintained" (Rev. 6:9).

10-38

Such a position directly contradicts the divine assurance, already mentioned above, that all who believe in Him (not just believers before the seventieth week) have the unconditional "hope of salvation [deliverance]."

10-39

If the day of the Lord were to begin at the opening of the seventieth week, Antichrist would prevail over the Lord for the majority of those seven years. While God was supposedly venting His wrath on earth, Antichrist would be expanding his satanic kingdom. And after Michael's restraint is removed at the midpoint of the week, Satan's minion would have still greater reign over the earth, even to the point of setting up his throne in God's Temple and demanding worship from the world.

10-40

If "the Lord alone shall be exalted" in the day of the Lord, as Isaiah so explicitly states, it is an irrational contradiction to believe that during the Lord's "own day," an unhindered Antichrist will be demanding and receiving the world's worship of himself.

10-41

Christ Himself — in the Olivet Discourse — confirms in answering His disciples that when the second seal of the "beginning birth pangs" is in process, "the end" — or "the end of the age" — will not yet have come. Christ had already explained that the "end of the age" will be when the tares are harvested and burned, a direct reference to the day of the Lord (Matthew 13:40).

10-42

The Lord Jesus told His disciples that the day of the Lord will not occur until *after* their tribulation. It is the one who *endures to the end (of the age) who shall be saved (delivered).*

10-43

Christ specifically says that "when you see all these things, recognize that He [Christ] is near, right at the door" (Matthew 24:33).

10-44

In the context of His promise, "these things" refers to all of the events up to and including the sign of the end of the age which comes "immediately after the tribulation of those days." Therefore the wrath of God cannot occur until after "these things" occur making it impossible to equate the seventieth week with the wrath of God.

Note: Some men, arguing that the seal events are the wrath of God, use Ezekiel 14:21 as a proof text for their argument. Because at face value there seems to be some merit to their argument, this author feels that it is important for us to understand why their argument cannot hold water, not only because all of the other teachings of Scripture concerning the timing of God's wrath — including Revelation 12:12 — but because a careful analysis of Ezekiel 14:21, on its own account, cannot support their argument.

10-45

Even though war, famine, wild animals, and plague correspond to the second, third, and fourth seals, we cannot conclude that these refer to God's wrath displayed during the day of the Lord in the end times. The first and fifth seals are not mentioned in the Ezekiel passage. The first seal represents false christs (Matthew 24:5), and the fifth seal represents the "martyrdom" of God's faithful elect (Revelation 6:9), which is associated with the great tribulation of Antichrist (Matthew 24:9,10). To attribute the first and fifth seal events (the primary target in both cases being the "faithful" elect of God [Luke 21:8; Matthew 24:21,22]) to the wrath of God would certainly be a "kingdom divided against itself" (Matthew 12:25-27).

10-46

Chemah. Chemah connotes hot displeasure or indignation.

10-47

Ebrah is the only term that is specifically used of God's day-of-the-Lord wrath. *Ebrah* is by far the strongest word and refers to the overflowing fury of God.

10-48

Its context is always God's wrath against the Gentile nations, not Israel.

10-49

God's wrath during the day of the Lord is primarily directed on the Gentile nations.

10-50

In this passage God's wrath is directed on Israel.

10-51

The first 6 seal events cannot be the wrath of God.

10-52

Satan!

10-53

The first seal, the white horse, must represent the proliferation of false messiahs, or christs, that will suddenly appear on the scene right after the covenant with death is signed by Israel. We are sure of this position because Christ's explains the meaning of the first seal to us in His Olivet Discourse.

10-54

Christ personally warns "Take heed that you be not misled." The false christs represented by the first seal will convince many people within the professing church that they (the false christs) are indeed the true Christ who has now returned to earth. They will claim His second coming! For this reason, the Lord's warning about those counterfeit messiahs is a clear and stern command to every believer: "YOU. . . do not go after them."

10-55

Severe spiritual and moral decay will have gripped the church in general long before Antichrist begins to operate. Because their leadership will lack spiritual discernment, because they will not have the resolution to teach the truth when it is unpopular, and because they will refuse to take the necessary measures to protect their congregations, many churches will be infested with false teaching.

10-56

They are spiritually dead.

10-57

They allegorize or simply dismiss prophetic Scripture.

10-58

They are taught they will be raptured before the seventieth week ever begins.

10-59

They will be prepared to survive the great persecution by Antichrist, just as Noah and his family were before the Flood, and just as Lot and his family were before the destruction of Sodom and Gomorrah.

10-60

The second seal will usher in a time of worldwide warfare such as the world has never known heretofore.

10-61

Antichrist will establish his position as a world leader by the defeat of his enemies, and he will try to consolidate the various nations and political factions who are willing to give him their allegiance.

10-62

The ten kings that make the final beast empire of Antichrist.

10-63

Tremendous worldwide food shortages.

10-64

Antichrist may very possibly take advantage of the worldwide famine by stockpiling grain and other non-perishable foodstuffs which will become a bargaining chip once he comes into complete world power and demands his mark for all who wish to buy or sell.

10-65

The beginning of birth pangs.

10-66

The first half of the seventieth week comes to an end.

10-67

The most likely candidate is the Babylonian Harlot - that is, the false religious system or systems that originated in Babylon, that system which Satan has used to deceive the nations concerning Christ (the true seed of the woman [Gen. 3:15]) in Satan's attempt to destroy the elect of God.

10-68

Although Scripture provides a number of clues, it does not specifically identify the Harlot in so many words.

10-69

The "woman" is a harlot. Spiritual harlotry, which is in mind in this passage, is always a reference to false gods and their false religions. In other words, the Babylonian Harlot represents, in part, a false religious system that competes with the true gospel of Christ.

10-70

The woman not only represents an actual false religion, but a false religion that has its roots in Babylon. The common denominator is some form of mother/child or mother/goddess (queen of heaven) worship.

10-71

This false religious system will set on many waters, which we are told represent peoples, multitudes, nations, and tongues. In other words, this false religious system will be worldwide, playing a dominant role in the lives of many.

10-72

The Harlot will also have political clout, so that the she "reigns over the kings of the earth."

10-73

This false religious system will vehemently oppose biblical Christianity - i.e., it will be "drunk with the blood of the saints and with the witnesses of Jesus."

10-74

This false religious system will also represent "the great city, which reigns over the kings of the earth."

10-75

The seven heads upon which the Harlot sits are not only the seven kings who will provide the leadership for the first seven beast empires, but also represents seven hills upon which this particular great city, with its religious affiliation to the Harlot, sits. Although we do not know what specific form the false religion of the Babylonian Harlot will take in the last days, we do know that the groundwork for its acceptance is already being laid by a growing revival of mother/child worship, especially within the Roman and Byzantine churches, which, interestingly, were false religious systems dominating cities built upon seven hills. Rome and Constantinople.

CHAPTER 11
ANTICHRIST REVEALED

11-1

The Jerusalem Campaign, the first invasion of Israel by Antichrist and his armies.

11-2

Isaiah 28:18; Ezekiel 38:8, 9, 11, 16; Zechariah 14:2. The Jews should be concerned because this is the event that will eventually cancel the covenant, bringing death to two out of three Jews then living in Israel.

11-3

"There will be a time of distress such as never occurred since there was a nation until that time"

11-4

Sheer Terror!

11-5

The "*Abomination of Desolation*" — Antichrist — takes his seat in the Temple and reveals himself as god.

11-6

It stems from Satan's intense conflict with God, the Jews being God's channel for the elect's redemption from the kingdom of Satan into the kingdom of God, which will culminate in the eventual defeat of Satan.

11-7

Some Jews in Israel, however, in particular those who have distrusted the covenant with Antichrist from the beginning, will heed the warning of their fellow countrymen, the Jewish witnesses. And before the armies of Antichrist begin to move around the city of Jerusalem during the Jerusalem Campaign, they will flee the city and hide in the wilderness place provided by God (Revelation 12:13, 14; Ezekiel 20:34, 35; Isaiah 16:1-4a).

11-8

No. For reasons known only to God, this area will be "rescued out of his hands."

11-9

In this very specific warning to the descendants of Esau, God threatens the Edomites with His impending day of the Lord, still to come after "the woman" flees to the wilderness to avoid the great tribulation by Antichrist.

11-10

The day of the Lord *must* follow the great tribulation or distress that begins at the midpoint of the seventieth week of Daniel.

11-11

"The woman" who flees to the wilderness during the Jerusalem Campaign will be a special group of 144,000 God-fearing Jews referred to as such only twice in Scripture, in Revelation chapters 7 and 14 (see endnote 1). The 144,000 will be a small remnant of Israel, twelve thousand coming from each of the twelve tribes of Jacob (Revelation 7:4-8). All of these will have refused to apostatize to Antichrist during the first half of the seventieth week, out of a fear of God, in general, although they will not yet know the reality of Christ in their lives when they flee to the wilderness at the mid-point of the week.

11-12

Satan, along with his angels, are thrown down to earth.

11-13

Satan will initiate the "time of distress such as never occurred since there was a nation (Israel) until that time" (Dan. 12:1), as Satan attempts to prevent the national salvation of Israel, the singular event that will complete the spiritual kingdom of God.

11-14

Satan's appearance upon earth will also initiate the time of "fiery testing" upon the church as Satan will be given direct access to the church, bringing upon "the elect of God" a "great tribulation such as not occurred since the beginning of the world until now, nor ever shall" (Matt. 24:21,22).

11-15

The beast — Antichrist. The world will respond by saying, "Who is like the beast, and who is able to wage war with him?"

11-16

Here we see unequivocally that the great tribulation is not an expression of the wrath of God, but of the "great wrath" of the devil and his persecution carried out through Antichrist.

11-17

The archangel, Michael.

11-18

'*Amad* means "to stand up" or "stand still." The verb '*amad* in Daniel 12:1 is ordinarily rendered as "will arise," "will stand up," or the like, but such a rendering makes little sense in the context of what immediately follows in that verse. After careful study of endnote 4 you will see that it seems most appropriate to translate Daniel 12:1, "stand still." In other words, Michael will not stand up, or arise, in preparation for the later defending Israel, but rather will "stand still" or "stop" doing what he normally does - that is, he will stop his activity of restraining the demonic forces of Satan thereby allowing Antichrist to reveal his true identity to the world and to vent his full fury on God's people.

11-19

The same word '*amad* is translated "stood still."

11-20

The "one who restrains" or the "Restrainer."

11-21

Daniel 10:21. The one who "stands firmly against" or "restrains."

11-22

No!

11-23

Satan unleashes his wrath against "the woman" and "the rest of her offspring, who keep the commandments of God and hold to the testimony of Jesus," during the great tribulation persecution by Antichrist.

11-24

Antichrist will be embolden and empowered by Satan to carry out the most hideous blasphemies and atrocities the world has ever known. The unbelieving world, recognizing who this dead man brought back to life really is — will be compelled to give him their absolute allegiance and worship.

11-25

Perhaps the most startling fact concerning Antichrist is that he is (or will be) a dead man brought back to life, one whose "fatal wound was healed."

11-26

1. Antichrist
2. The beast
3. The man of lawlessness and the son of destruction
4. Gog
5. The little horn

6. An extremely powerful and ungodly king
7. The destroyer
8. The extortioner
9. The head of the house of evil
10. The personified abomination of desolation

11-27

This is clearly a reference to a person, not a nation, since only an individual could stand in this holy place.

11-28

It depends on how the term is used in each specific context.

11-29

Egypt, Assyria, Babylon, Medo-Persia, Greece ("five have fallen").

11-30

Rome under Nero, ("one is").

11-31

Most probably the Nazi Empire of the Third Reich under Adolph Hitler.

11-32

There will be an eighth leader who will lead the final ten-nation confederation — namely Antichrist, who "was and is not," and who is also "one of the seven" rulers of the preceding seven beast empires.

11-33

He is a dead man who comes from the abyss, brought back to life to rule over the final beast empire of Satan.

11-34

Antichrist will be a man who will claim to be God incarnate.

11-35

He will be a man who will be an extremely powerful and ungodly military leader.

11-36

He will be a man who will be given the diabolical power of Satan himself.

11-37

He will be a man who is the dead leader of one of the seven previous beast empires of Satan.

11-38

He will be a man who was killed by a fatal wound to the head with a military weapon or "sword."

11-39

He will be a dead man who will come back to life to rule the final beast empire of Satan.

11-40

He will be a man who will receive the absolute allegiance and worship of the world when they realize that he is a dead man brought back to life.

11-41

He will be a man who is from the ancestral line of Magog.

11-42

A man whose soul comes up out of Hades.

11-43

None of these leaders come from the ancestral line of Magog.

11-44

The sixth beast empire, Rome, or Hitler's empire known as the Third Reich, or the third empire of Germany.

11-45

Because of his fierce hatred of both Jews and Christians, Nero is probably the best candidate for the ruler of the Roman Beast Empire. It was under his instruction that Titus began his systematic campaign against Israel in A.D. 67.

11-46

The diabolical leader, Adolph Hitler who persecuted the Jews while they were scattered throughout the world without a homeland. Notably, Hitler's ancestry is Japhetic, from the line of Magog.

11-47

1. Antichrist must have been a leader of a former beast empire (Revelation 13:3; 17:11). Both Nero and Hitler meet this criterion.
2. Antichrist must have died by a "wound of the sword" (Revelation 13:14). Neither Nero nor Hitler died literally by the sword, but both died by weapons used in warfare, and Hitler in particular took his life during battle rather than surrender.
3. Antichrist will be from "the land of Magog" (Ezekiel 38:2), which is a perfect description of Hitler, who not only was from the geographical area of Magog, but also came from the ancestral lineage of Magog. And because Rome was founded by the nomadic tribes of Magog, Meshech, or Tubal, it is uncertain as to which of these peoples he descended from, although the author would be inclined to think that Nero was Magogite as well.

11-48

4. Antichrist will be a notorious anti-Semite (Matthew 24:15-21; Revelation 12:13-17). Hitler is the supreme anti-Semite of history. Nero despised Jews, but he hated all non-Romans in general, and unlike Hitler, he had no consuming desire to specifically destroy all Jews.
5. Antichrist will be immediately recognized - and it will be the immediate recognition of this man brought back to life that will amaze the world to the point that the world will follow after him (Revelation 13:3; 17:8). Hitler would easily qualify in that regard, whereas Nero would not.

11-49

Adolph Hitler, the Magogite ruler of the seventh beast empire of Satan.

11-50

If Christ's offer of the physical kingdom of God upon earth had been accepted by the nation of Israel at His first coming, (Christ would still have been "cut off" and the city and sanctuary destroyed [Dan. 9:26]) but the interval between the sixty-ninth and seventieth weeks would have been a matter of years, not centuries. Nero then would have become the Antichrist of the final beast empire of Satan, and the seventh beast empire described in Revelation 17 after the Diaspora had begun, would have never become a reality.

11-51

Hitler's pact with the devil, his delusion as the new messianic savior, his veneration "above every so-called god or object of worship" (see 2 Thessalonians 2:4), his dream of a "thousand year Reich," his satanic desire to annihilate every one of God's chosen people - all correspond precisely to the character of the man who will be the Antichrist of the end times.

CHAPTER 12
COUNTING THE COST

12-1

The power of the beast will extend over "the whole earth." There is no question that the whole world will worship Antichrist when he gains control of the earth at the midpoint of the seventieth week.

12-2

"Everyone whose name has not been written from the foundation of the world in the book of life of the Lamb who has been slain." Obviously, those of Israel whom God has chosen from the foundation of the world will refuse the mark, even though in unbelief, and will come to Christ at their appointed time immediately following the completion of the seventieth week.

12-3

Each person will be commanded to make his own individual image "to the beast."

12-4

Image can be rendered just as appropriately as "statue."

12-5

Yes, the Greek text gives us the right to interpret this passage with the view that each individual will make his own statue, rather than co-operate in the manufacture of just one international statue. The Greek term translated "image" in this text can be taken (and here is best taken) as a collective singular, like our English words "crowd" or "people." Therefore, when image is used as a collective noun, by definition it must refer to a great number of separate images or statues.

12-6

The very next verse — 16 — uses the word "hand" which, likewise, is clearly in the collective singular mode, as well. Therefore, because the context of the passage has already used the collective singular mode for "hand," it, likewise, can be used and should be used for the word "image" as well, referring to multiple images, not just one.

12-7

Gold, silver, brass, stone or wood.

12-8

The Greek term here rendered "breath" is rarely translated that way but is usually rendered as "spirit" and sometimes as "life." The meaning of this passage, then, is that after the world is commanded to build their own "images" to Antichrist, some form of spirit or life will be put within these "images," so "that the image of the beast might even speak and cause as many as do not worship the image of the beast to be killed!"

12-9

Fortunately those demonic images, despite their fearsome powers, will be blind, deaf, and immobile - unable to see, hear, or walk.

12-10

Each demon's movement will be limited by the inanimate object it indwells which would seem to allow the possibility that true Christians, as well as others who refuse to bow down to the images, will have some chance to avoid detection and destruction.

12-11

1. Demons require some physical object, animate or inanimate, through which to operate.
2. We learn that the demons spoke through the men they indwelt.
3. Although demons are restricted to the objects they indwell, they are able to create great havoc both within and through those objects.
4. Demons seem to have no ability to choose their physical abodes.

12-12

The images will be suddenly indwelt by the horde of Satan's fallen angels and demonic spirits that will have been cast down to earth just prior to that time.

12-13

As Christians it will be absolutely essential that we do not go near these images or enter any place where they are present - so that the images have no opportunity to "speak" and identify us, or to "cause [us who] do not worship the image of the beast to be killed" (Revelation 13:15b).

12-14

1. Everyone will be required to "worship the image of the beast [or] be killed."
2. Everyone will be required to take the mark of the beast or he will be unable to buy or sell anything.

12-15

The potential of death for not worshipping the beast or one of his images, and the inability to purchase or sell anything unless one has taken Antichrist's mark on his hand or forehead.

12-16

Absolutely. Without food and without the mark to buy his food, those refusing the mark will die or will have to have an alternative food supply, in advance.

12-17

"They will fall away from the faith, paying attention to deceitful spirits and doctrines of demons."

12-18

Their idols of silver and gold will not be able to deliver them during the day of God's wrath, the day of the Lord.

12-19

Because they "have kept the word of My perseverance."

12-20

Hupomone has the basic meaning of hiding under, of patient enduring and fortitude, or of remaining behind. Within the sphere of God's grace, it is the faithful believer's keeping of "My [Christ's] perseverance" that brings believers through "the hour of testing."

12-21

Three divinely dispatched angels of God.

12-22

The message of the first angel will be the eternal gospel which is the gospel of Jesus Christ, the same gospel proclaimed through out all of Scriptures.

12-23

It is the only hope for lost mankind.

12-24

In order for a man to become right before God, he must turn from (repent) his sin and turn to (believe in) Jesus Christ as his only means of salvation.

12-25

It fulfills Christ's prophecy that "this gospel of the kingdom shall be preached in the whole world . . . and then the end [of the age] will come." Those of the world whom the missionaries fail to reach, the first angel will certainly reach, and the whole world will be without excuse, going into the last half of the seventieth week.

12-26

The second angel will announce to the world that the Babylonian Harlot - Satan's false religious system - has been destroyed by Antichrist.

12-27

Antichrist must destroy his temporary ally, the Babylonian Harlot (the foreign god of Daniel 11:39), because in his claim to deity, he cannot tolerate any rival.

12-28

Antichrist and his ungodly ten-nation coalition that compromise the final beast empire of Satan.

12-29

Because, in his claim to deity, Antichrist cannot tolerate any rival. Once Antichrist sets himself up as God, even this false religious system(s), and those representative of her false system(s), must and will be destroyed since Antichrist will allow nothing to compete with him for the world's worship and absolute allegiance.

12-30

The Babylonian Harlot is the false religious system(s) (the mother/child worship that originated in Babylon).
Babylon the Great (city) is the corrupt city situated on seven hills, that has aligned herself with the Harlot, the false religious system of the last days.

12-31

The Babylonian Harlot will be destroyed at the mid-point of the seventieth week.

12-32

The Babylon the Great (city) at the seventh bowl judgment (see chapter 20).

12-33

The pronouncement of the third angel will set forth the only two alternatives about which all living souls will be compelled to decide. Worship the beast or his image and you will live today but will spend eternity in the Lake of Fire; or refuse the beast or his image and you risk death today but will spend eternity with Christ.

12-34

Future.

12-35

The consequences for submitting to Antichrist during the great tribulation — having to go through God's wrath (the day of the Lord) which is still to follow — proves that the wrath of God *follows* the great tribulation of Antichrist. As the great tribulation of Antichrist begins at the midpoint of the seventieth week, any attempt to equate the entire seventieth week with the day of the Lord clearly contradicts the critical message of the third angel!

12-36

Their ministry will begin at the beginning of the last three and a half years.

12-37

1. God will use them to "prophecy" - to proclaim the approaching condemnation on those who submit to Antichrist and to call their fellow Jews to repentance and faith in Jesus Christ, their true Messiah, Redeemer and King.
2. God will use them "to smite the earth with every plague, as often as they desire."

12-38

They will witness for exactly twelve hundred and sixty days or three and a half years.

12-39

They most likely will be Elijah and Moses.

CHAPTER 13
THE GREAT TRIBULATION BY ANTICHRIST

13-1

This will be a time of distress and persecution that is greater than either Israel or the church in general has ever known before. The great tribulation of Antichrist will go far beyond anything that has ever "occurred since the beginning of the world."

13-2

It will begin at the mid-point of the seventieth week. At the three and one half year mark.

13-3

The Devil's wrath through his minion, Antichrist (the beast).

13-4

The woman that flees to the wilderness (the nation Israel), and the rest of her offspring (the professing church at large).

13-5

"The woman" of Revelation 12:17 represents a relatively small group of God-fearing Jews who refuse to acknowledge the covenant made with Antichrist and therefore heed the warnings to flee from Jerusalem (as well as from other nations of the world).

13-6

In the wilderness to which they have fled.

13-7

First fruits to God and to the Lamb.

13-8

As the 144,000.

13-9

Spiritually chaste. In other words, these are the one who refuse to acknowledge — apostatize to Antichrist — during the first half of the seventieth week.

13-10

Genuine Christians, the true church, compromised of both Jew and Gentile.

13-11

Because "the woman" represents "God-fearing Israel," and because the rest of her offspring "keep the commandments of God and hold to the testimony of Jesus," this rules out that portion of Israel that succumb to Antichrist, as well as that portion of Israel in general that honored the covenant but refused to bow to Antichrist, because she is still unsaved at this point (the midpoint of the seventieth week), and does not come to know Christ personally until after the seventieth week is complete. Therefore, the only group that remains, that "keep the commandments of God and hold to the testimony of Jesus" at the midpoint of the seventieth week, is the true church, both Jew and Gentile.

13-12

Because other than the 144,000, the first fruits, the remainder of Israel will not come to know Christ until the end of the seventieth week.

13-13

Galatians 3:29 tells us that all believers are "the spiritual offspring of Abraham."

13-14

The elect of God will be delivered to tribulation, and they will kill you, and you will be hated by all nations on account of My name.

13-15

"On account of my Name." In other words, the elect of God, the faithful, will identify with Christ rather than take the mark, and worship the image of the beast.

13-16

"Many will fall away," and "most people's love will grow cold."

13-17

The church at large is a compromising church for the most part, holding to a form of godliness but denying its power.

13-18

Death, associated with the great tribulation of Antichrist.

13-19

Whom they will serve. The faithful will serve only Christ, even if it costs them their lives. The unfaithful will "fall away" and their love for Christ will "grow cold," preserve their physical life, but losing their eternal soul.

13-20

The Seraphim.

13-21

Today with the earth's population estimated at 5 billion, a quarter of the earth's population perfectly fits the description of the church, in general, that claims the name of Christ. Approximately 600 million claim Roman Catholicism, another 150 million are associated with Eastern Orthodoxy, and approximately 250 million would claim to be Protestant. Obviously, although all of these church organizations claim the name of Christ, the majority of church members today would, in reality, fit the description of the church of Sardis (Rev. 3:1).

13-22

The separation of the tares from the wheat.

13-23

Death or Hell — represent the choice that every professing Christian will have during the great persecution of Antichrist. Refuse to worship the image of the beast and the result is Death — you will die. On the other hand, worship the image and you will spend eternity in Hell (Rev. 14:9, 10, 13).

13-24

When comparing these passages together, it soon becomes apparent that Antichrist will threaten those claiming the name of Christ, using civil authorities now aligned with Satan's evil purposes.

13-25

If proper prior provision has not been made, those who claim the name of Christ will have to either die by famine (because of the lack of food) or take the mark of Antichrist in order to buy food they need, at the expense of their eternal right standing before God.

13-26

The Greek word translated "wild beasts" in this key text is used 38 times in the book of Revelation. Except for this one instance, in every other case it is simply translated "beast" and refers to either Antichrist (13:3,4), to the second beast that assists Antichrist (13:11), or to the images of the beast (13:15). Therefore, in the context of the fourth seal, and because the definite article is used before the Greek word translated "wild beasts," (i.e. "the" wild beasts, which must therefore refer to specific beasts mentioned in the context of the book of Revelation), this writer assumes that this specific mode of death "by the wild beasts of the earth," will be the death associated with the elect's refusal to worship the image of the "beast," or the beast himself as provided for by the second beast (Revelation 13:11-15).

13-27

The civil authorities representing the beast, the absence of the mark of the beast, and the refusal to worship the beast.

Note: There is a fourth method of death listed, translated "pestilence" in the NAS, but this translation is not a proper translation. The Greek word that the NAS translates "pestilence" is the same word that describes the fourth horseman, and it means "death," and only death. Pestilence is an entirely different Greek word.

13-28

Those of the nation of Israel who supported the covenant with Antichrist initially, shunning their opportunity to flee when they could, and yet who will not bow down and worship the beast or his image once his true identity is known.

13-29

The rural areas of Israel (the clans of Judah), or in the remote, protective areas in either the land of Egypt or the land of Assyria.

13-30

Two-thirds of the nation of Israel will die.

13-31

Fifty percent! Half of the city.

13-32

This group will be Jewish witnesses who will call their fellow countrymen to repentance, starting at the beginning of the seventieth week.

13-33

They will be hauled into court, beaten, betrayed by their own parents and by their own children, hated by their fellow Jews, forced to flee from one city to the next, yet will faithfully proclaim the name of Christ to their fellow countrymen in Israel until the end of the age.

13-34

The verse ends by saying, "until the Son of Man comes."

13-35

In this author's opinion, those Jewish witnesses who die in pursuit of the souls of their fellow Jewish countrymen are the martyrs.

13-36

These martyrs may also include other faithful Christians ("their fellow servants") who, before the day of the Lord commences, likewise choose to lay down their lives for the sake of the lost or the compromising church in other parts of the world, paralleling the work of the Jewish witnesses in the land of Israel.

13-37

No. This group does not include the multitude of believers who will die from within the compromising church because of their complete lack of preparedness for the great tribulation of Antichrist. Although many compromising believers will suffer martyrdom, it will not be because "of the testimony which they had maintained," but rather because of the testimony they compromised in their unfaithfulness in both life and doctrine.

13-38

So that the church will be presented to Christ as His bride "in all her glory, having no spot or wrinkle . . . that she should be holy and blameless" "so that when He appears, we may have confidence and not shrink away from Him in shame at His coming."

13-39

The separation of the tares from the wheat.

13-40

"At that time many will fall away and . . . most people's [professing Christians] love will grow cold."

13-41

God must "purify for Himself a people for His own possession," "that the proof of your faith, being more precious than gold which is perishable, even though tested by fire, may be found to result in praise and glory and honor at the revelation of Jesus Christ!"

13-42

1. Assurance of their salvation, "so that you may be considered worthy of the kingdom of God (2 Thessalonians 1:4,5).
2. The assurance of glory (1 Peter 4:16-17a; 5:1,4).
3. So that we may develop patience and endurance (Luke 17:22-24,26,27,30; 18:1-8; Romans 5:3-5,9).

13-43

The great tribulation by Antichrist.

13-44

No. The martyrs were crying out in a loud voice, asking "How long?" The context is definitely asking when God would retaliate against Satan and his forces.

13-45

The Seraphim are not involved with this fifth seal because the process of purification and refinement of the church (overseen by God's Seraphim) will be complete.

13-46

Because the wrath of God cannot begin until "the number of their fellow servants and their brethren who were to be killed, even as they had been, should be completed also.

13-47

On a day and an hour that no one knows, only the Father alone, when God "cuts short" the great tribulation of Antichrist, but not before the "number of their brethren" is complete.

13-48

They had no comprehension of the great gap between the sixty-ninth and the seventieth weeks of Daniel's vision.

13-49

Jesus said, "If I want him to remain until I come, what is that to you?"

13-50

Many Christians in the early church expected the overthrow of Rome (the legs of iron and the empire that then oppressed them) to be the next major event in God's prophetic calendar. Thus they thought that the overthrow of Rome could occur at any moment, never suspecting the long gap between the impending destruction of both the city and the sanctuary and the commencement of the seventieth week (Dan. 9:26-27).

13-51

We are to look expectantly for the last seven years to begin, and for the events that will then lead up to the return of Christ. But at the same time, Jesus did not teach that His return would be soon. In either case, the most important thing is that we (like Peter) follow Him.

13-52

To live with a strong sense of <u>expectancy</u>, always being alert and sober, always looking with anticipation for the events that will lead up to the end times, and always being prepared for the day of the Lord once these events have come to pass.

13-53

Christians through the ages have always understood the words of Christ to have a much broader meaning. . . . In other words, the present tense can best be explained as a means of rhetorical inclusiveness that does not exclude those who are not specifically addressed, but embraces a much wider meaning (i.e., every believer in every age).

CHAPTER 14
THE SIGN OF THE END OF THE AGE

14-1

1. "When will these things be?" referred to Christ's statement that "not one stone [of the Temple] here shall be left upon another, which will not be torn down" (Matthew 24:2). In other words, the destruction of the Temple by Titus in 70 A.D.
2. "What will be the sign of Your coming?" This question refers exactly to what it says. When will Christ return? His second coming.
3. "What will be the sign of . . . the end of the age?" (Matthew 24:3). A reference to when the day of the Lord — God's wrath — would begin (see Matthew 13:40).

14-2

The first question is answered in Luke 21:12-24, and the other two questions are answered in both Matthew 24 and Luke 21. Together, these two passages give the best summary of Christ's Olivet Discourse to His disciples.

14-3

On the afternoon of the third day.

14-4

Because the disciples were beginning to realize that Christ was indeed going to leave them, but that He would also return the next time to judge the nations.

14-5

When the tares are gathered up and burned, so shall it be at the end of the age.

14-6

The day of the Lord.

14-7

Absolutely, in fact the explanation concerning the end of the age was instruction specifically for them.

14-8

First, at the coming of Christ, the righteous will be rescued — as with Noah and Lot — and then God will pour out judgment.

14-9

Do not be deceived by the "great signs and wonders" that false christs and false prophets will perform during the great tribulation by Antichrist.

14-10

When the great tribulation by Antichrist is "cut short" by the sign of the end of the age.

14-11

Koloboo. A medical term to describe the amputation of a leg, arm, or other body part. In general use, it meant to curtail or to shorten.

14-12

It is not that *time period* that will be cut short but rather *the persecution* by Antichrist against God's elect, which will occur within the forty-two months (starting at the beginning), but will be "cut short" before the time period comes to an end.

14-13

"The sun will be darkened, and the moon will not give its light, and the stars will fall from the sky, and the powers of the heavens will be shaken."

14-14

The sign of the sun, moon and stars.

14-15

After the sign of the day of the Lord is given in the heavens, both passages state when the day of the Lord will transpire. Immediately afterwards.

14-16

Absolutely!

14-17

The sign will appear, "immediately after the tribulation of those days" (Matthew 24:29) and "before the great and awesome day of the Lord" (Joel 2:31). Christ explicitly links together the sign of the end of the age which occurs "immediately after the tribulation" (Matt. 24:29b) with the sign prophesied in the Old Testament announcing the day of the Lord, which will occur when the great tribulation by Antichrist is "cut short."

14-18

The second sign is "the sign of the Son of Man"

14-19

It "will appear in the sky" and will follow in immediate succession to the sign of the end of the age.

14-20

1. The day of the Lord will be preceded by two successive stunning signs - the sign of the end of the age and the sign of Christ's coming.
2. Both of these signs (and the events they announce) will occur after the tribulation — or more correctly *when* the tribulation is cut short (see Matthew 24:22).
3. Both of these signs are given *before* the coming of the Son of Man on the clouds of the sky.

14-21

It clearly shows that the Rapture will not occur until after the tribulation, at the point when the great tribulation of Antichrist is cut short sometime during the second half of the last "week" of Daniel.

14-22

The number of the faithful Christian martyrs is complete.

14-23

There will be "dismay among the nations, in perplexity at the roaring of the sea and the waves, men fainting from fear and the expectation of things [God's wrath soon to follow] which are coming upon the world."

14-24

Those of the kingdom of God, the overcomers, will look up with great joy and expectancy, knowing that "when these things begin to take place . . . your redemption is drawing near."

14-25

The world will have been warned by the third angel of their impending disaster if they worship the beast or his image.

14-26

1. Satan's "deception of wickedness for those who perish."
2. And because "God will send upon them a deluding influence so that they might believe what is false, in order that they may be judged who did not believe the truth, but took pleasure in wickedness."

14-27

God will gather the nations and bring them down to the valley of Jehoshaphat.

14-28

God's judgment, the day of the Lord judgment of the kingdom of darkness.

14-29

The Jehoshaphat Campaign.

14-30

1. The Jerusalem Campaign
2. The Jehoshaphat Campaign
3. The Armageddon Campaign

14-31

The Jerusalem Campaign will occur at the midpoint of the seventieth week, at which time Antichrist will move his armies against Jerusalem, set up his throne in the Temple, and demand the world's worship.

14-32

The Jehoshaphat Campaign is a precursor to the day of the Lord and the return of Christ. This Campaign will occur sometime during the second half of the seventieth week, just prior to when the great tribulation by Antichrist is cut short by God's day-of-the-Lord wrath.

14-33

Armageddon will take place after the seventieth week is complete, at the end of the day of the Lord some thirty days later. This will involve primarily the ungodly armies of the eighth beast empire and their battle against the righteous forces of Christ.

14-34

Immediately before the Lord takes His saints to be with Himself, the unbelieving world will be living in peace and security under Antichrist's protection. Suddenly and without warning an astounding sign in the heavens will appear announcing God's day of wrath and bringing terror into every person's heart except the elect of God. . . . This will be the sign of the end of the age, vividly described in Revelation as the breaking of the sixth seal.

14-35

Revelation 6:17, "has come."

14-36

The Greek word *elthen* is the aorist tense indicative mood of *erchomai*, the most common Greek verb for "come." Looking at the explanations of the Greek scholars quoted in the endnote we find that the context determines the tense of the aorist verb. Because the word wrath is not mentioned in the book of Revelation prior to the sixth seal, and because the signs given in the sun, moon and stars, mentioned in relationship to the sixth seal, perfectly parallel the signs that will occur announcing the day of the Lord's wrath, and because the word "wrath" is mentioned numerous times in the chapters that follow in relationship to events directly associated with the seventh seal, the context of Revelation 6:17 seems self-evident. The wrath of God is about to begin. And when the seventh seal is opened, it will!

14-37

Mark 14:41: "Are you still sleeping and taking your rest? Is it enough; the hour has come (*elthen*); behold the Son of Man is being betrayed into the hands of sinners."

14-38

In Mark 14:41, Jesus is speaking of His impending death which obviously has not yet taken place but rather is about to come. In Revelation 6:17 Jesus is speaking about His wrath which has not yet taken place but is about to come.

CHAPTER 15
THE SIGN OF CHRIST'S COMING

15-1

The sign of Christ's coming is the "lightning" that "comes from the east and flashes even to the west."

15-2

The lightning is a reference to the glory of God.

15-3

After the natural lights are turned off all over the world, the supernatural light of God's holy splendor will return to earth from the east, flooding the world with the radiance of Christ as He returns in power and great glory.

15-4

"Behold, He is coming with the clouds, and every eye will see Him, even those who pierced Him."

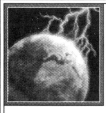

15-5

The word rendered "is revealed" in this passage, is the Greek verb *apokalupto*, which refers basically to a revealing or uncovering, but may also express the idea of manifestation.

15-6

The Greek word is *epiphaneia* and expresses the idea of "a shining forth."

15-7

The Greek word is *phaneroo* which can carry the idea of "lighten" or "shine."

15-8

When we take these terms together, we get a sense of how dramatic and spectacular the coming of Christ will be. His coming will be a "manifestation," a "revealing," a sudden "appearance"; it will be accompanied by a shining brightness, His glory.

15-9

Because of God's superabundant grace, believers not only will rejoice in the manifested glory of their Savior and "stand in the presence of His glory, blameless with great joy," but will even be actual partakers of that glory, as well.

15-10

Isaiah 2:2, 12, 19; 60:1-3; Zechariah 2:5-10; Psalm 97:1-6.

15-11

God's glory first departed the Temple and the "midst of the city," and then secondly, it went up and stood over the "mountain which is east of the city."

15-12

It becomes quickly evident that the Lord's glory will return in exactly the reverse order and path by which it departed! It will return first when Christ is revealed at His second coming and later when He returns to rule over Israel.

CHAPTER 16
THE PREWRATH RAPTURE OF THE CHURCH: PART I

16-1

The correct timing of the Rapture is clearly revealed by Christ in His Olivet Discourse, is confirmed through Paul in his Thessalonian Epistles, and verified further by John in the book of Revelation.

16-2

Because all of the prophecies concerning Christ's first coming were fulfilled literally in every detail.

16-3

Christ will rapture His church *immediately after* He cuts short the great tribulation by Antichrist and *immediately before* He unleashes His day-of-the-Lord judgment on the ungodly world.

16-4

1. The Rapture will occur on the same day that the Lord begins to pour out His wrath of judgment on the world.
2. These back-to-back events (rapture and judgment) can only occur when God cuts short the great tribulation of Antichrist.

16-5

Christ could return at "any moment" since His departure as recorded in Acts 1:9-11. According to the imminency view, nothing prophetically that has had to occur since the Ascension, since Christ's second coming has always been imminent, that is it could occur at any moment.

16-6

One leading pretribulationalist has said, "Neither a pretribulation nor a posttribulation rapture is an explicit teaching of Scripture" and another, "Perhaps the position of pretribulationism is correct although its proof at times has been logically invalid or at least unconvincing."

16-7

The day of the Lord cannot occur until Israel is back in her own land. And as the wrath of God is against the unrighteous inhabitants and armies of Satan's earthly kingdom, Antichrist and his eighth beast empire must likewise be on the world scene when Christ returns for Rapture and judgment. Therefore, if the rapture of the church and the day of the Lord occur on the same day, the imminent return of Christ has been impossible for the past two thousand years.

16-8

Luke 17:22-24, 26-30.

16-9

The argument is made that the phrase "after seven more days, I will send rain on the earth" means that Noah and his family entered the ark seven days before God's wrath came. Therefore, what Christ specifically says occurred on the same day, they maintain did not actually happen on the same day, but instead included a seven-day gap.

16-10

Such a conclusion not only contradicts the clear teaching of Christ, it is based upon Scripture clearly taken out of context. For as the Genesis text goes on to explain, Noah's entering the ark with his family was in fact "on the very same day" that "the fountains of the deep burst open."

16-11

By the way they ask the question, "Tell us, when will these things be, and what will be the sign of Your coming, and of the end of the age?"

16-12

Exactly as illustrated by Christ in His Olivet Discourse to His disciples, Peter likens Christ's return with the impending wrath that follows, to the days of Noah and Lot. First the faithful are rescued and then the wicked are destroyed. Back-to-back events.

16-13

The Greek word for "temptation" is *peirasmos* and it is better translated in Revelation 3:10 and 1 Peter 4:12 as "testing." The word carries the basic meaning of putting to the proof. In each case the believer is present during the testing, the great tribulation by Antichrist when all believers will be put to the proof, yet promised deliverance before the wrath of God begins. Peter simply repeats what he had been taught by his Lord.

16-14

The meaning of this passage in this context clearly is that those who are "taken" are taken to be with the Lord at the Rapture when He comes (see 1 Thess. 4:15), and those who are left, are left for judgment "like [in] the days of Noah" — again indicating that the Rapture and judgment will occur back to back.

16-15

Paralambano means "to take to oneself, to receive near, that is, to associate with oneself (in any familiar or intimate act or relation)."

16-16

In John 14:3 Jesus uses *paralambano* when He says; "I will come again, and *receive [paralambano]* you to Myself."

16-17

Yes, it would be confusing. However, the most literal understanding of Matthew 24:40,41 clearly is a reference to exactly the same truth described in John 14:1-3.

16-18

Paul explains that the Rapture will occur when the day of the Lord begins.

16-19

This reference to "a thief in the night" links together four other passages all of which refer to the Lord coming in judgment, as found in Luke 12:39, 40; 2 Peter 3:10; Revelation 3:3 and 16:15.

16-20

Christ will return to simultaneously rapture the church and unleash His wrath of judgment upon the ungodly. We must therefore conclude that nothing will separate the Rapture and the beginning of judgment when Christ returns on the day of the Lord.

16-21

Yes!

16-22

The return of Christ has never been imminent and will never be imminent until the great tribulation of Antichrist begins and the surrounding Gentile nations come together against Jerusalem in the valley of Jehoshaphat.

16-23

When the great tribulation by Antichrist is "cut short."

16-24

Yes. It is important to understand that the Rapture and the beginning of the day of the Lord occur on the same day, but it is far more important to understand, as the New Testament clearly teaches, that Christ's second coming will not occur until after the great tribulation by Antichrist has begun.

16-25

1. The Greek noun *parousia* has the primary meaning of "presence," and often the derived connotation of "coming or advent" - that is, of becoming present by one's arrival or appearance. In other words, the term itself does not carry the idea of movement, although that idea is often implied.
2. The verb *heko* has the basic meaning of "to come" or "to be present." In reference to Christ's second coming it is used only three times in the New Testament (Revelation 2:25; 3:3).
3. The verb, which has no corresponding noun, is always used of persons and specifically connotes movement, either coming or going, from one point to another. It is in contrast to *heko*, which denotes only arrival.

16-26

This particular word does not indicate movement from one place to the next, but, as a noun, speaks more to the overall event of Christ's second coming. It carries the basic meaning of "presence." Therefore, within the scope of the second coming (*parousia*) of Christ as an event, there will be various coming and goings of Christ, but in those cases a different Greek word is used.

16-27

The context of the book of Matthew demands that it is a book written for the church, not unsaved Israel.

16-28

The Great Commission (Matthew 28:19,20) has always been taken as Christ's instructions to the church.

16-29

Part of His instruction to the disciples is, "teaching them [the new disciples of all nations] to observe *all* that I have commanded you;" which makes it obvious that Christ intended for all of His teaching to be taught to all of His followers (the church) until "the end of the age."

16-30

Matthew is the only Gospel writer to record Jesus' use of the term "church" (Matthew 16:18; 18:15-20).

16-31

The Olivet Discourse was given on the third day of Passover, three days before He was crucified, just before Jesus' institution of the Lord's Supper (Matthew 26:26-29), which was given on the sixth day of Passover.

16-32

The Rapture.

16-33

It is obviously of great significance that much of Jesus' most important instruction, including the Olivet Discourse, to His followers - that is, the church - was given during or near Passover, which instruction would be foundational, not simply for the apostles and other church leaders but for all His followers.

16-34

First, Jesus described the "birth pangs" (Matthew 24:4-8), then He described the "great tribulation" (vv. 9-26), and then He described His glorious *parousia* (vv. 27-30) for rapture (v. 31) and for judgment (vv. 32-51).

16-35

"Immediately after the tribulation of those days," which, as Christ had already promised, would be "cut short . . . for the sake of the elect" (v. 22).

16-36

The coming (*parousia*) of Christ and our "gathering together" (Rapture) to Him.

16-37

In perfect harmony with the Olivet Discourse, Christ's coming (*parousia*) at the day of the Lord will only occur after the apostasy.

16-38

"The man of lawlessness (Antichrist) is revealed."

16-39

Antichrist takes his seat in the temple and demands the world's worship.

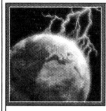

16-40

The restrainer, most probably Michael the archangel (see Daniel 10:21; 12:1; Revelation 12:7 and chapter 11, endnote 4).

16-41

Christ will bring Antichrist "to an end by the appearance of His coming (*parousia*)."

16-42

In perfect harmony with the Olivet Discourse, Christ's coming (*parousia*) at the day of the Lord will only occur *after* the apostasy (v. 3a), *after* the man of lawlessness (Antichrist) is revealed (v. 3b), and *after* Antichrist takes his seat in the temple and demands the world's worship (v.4). Only then will Christ bring Antichrist "to an end by the appearance of His coming [*parousia*]" (v. 8).

16-43

1. The context of the last two verses is Christ's "coming," His *parousia* (Matthew 24:3, 27).
2. His coming (*parousia*) will be associated with "the clouds" (v. 30).
3. His coming (*parousia*) will be associated with a "great trumpet" (v. 31).
4. His coming (*parousia*) will involve "His angels" who will gather "His elect form the four winds, from one end of the sky to the other" (v. 31).

16-44

1. The events occur at the "coming" (*parousia*) of Christ.
2. His coming (*parousia*) will in like manner be announced "with the trumpet of God."
3. At the coming (*parousia*) of Christ, the Lord will come "in the clouds" (cf Acts 1:9-11).
4. The fourth truth is implied by Paul's passive phrase "shall be caught up together." Because believers will be "caught up . . . to meet the Lord . . . in the air" it is implied that someone or some ones will "catch them up" and carry them to Him.

16-45

His angels, the reapers.

16-46

When the Son of Man comes in the glory of His Father, He will come with His angels.

16-47

They are identical.

16-48

1. The Rapture of the church and the beginning of the day of the Lord will occur back to back, on "the same day that the Son of Man is revealed."
2. The coming (*parousia*) of Christ occurs immediately after the great tribulation by Antichrist is cut short by God.
3. The exact same truths are taught consistently in the New Testament concerning how and when these events will take place.

CHAPTER 17
THE PREWRATH RAPTURE OF THE CHURCH: PART II

17-1

Chapter 6 outlines the events of the first half of the seventieth week (the first three seals), as well as the death and martyrdom of genuine Christians that comes as a result of the great tribulation by Antichrist that initiates the second half of the seventieth week (the fourth and fifth seals). The sixth seal recorded in chapter 6 then depicts the sign of the day of the Lord (when the natural light of the sun, moon, and stars is extinguished), when the great tribulation is cut short by God.

17-2

Revelation 7 is an interlude that occurs between the account of the sixth seal at the end of the sixth chapter (the sign of the day of the Lord) and the account of the seventh seal which actually initiates the day of the Lord at the beginning of chapter 8.

17-3

"All the angels," "the elders," and the "four living creatures."

17-4

The church is noticeably absent.

17-5

In verse 9 we are told that these are the ones "from every nation and all tribes and peoples and tongues."

17-6

Revelation 5:9. This multitude is described as those for whom Christ "wast slain, and didst purchase for God with Thy [Christ'] blood from every tribe and tongue and people and nation," the elect of God from all ages including the church!

17-7

Verse 14 says succinctly that "These are the ones who come out of the great tribulation."

17-8

This great multitude, can only be the elect of God for whom Christ died, who have just been raptured out of the great tribulation by Antichrist, after the sign of the end of the age is given at the sixth seal.

Note: In an attempt to confuse the obvious, pretribulationists will tell you that this great multitude does not all arrive at one time, but rather, is a group of Gentile martyrs that is getting larger and larger, as the great tribulation progresses and more Gentile converts are being slain by Antichrist. However, integrity with the Greek text will not permit that position.

17-9

There is absolutely no reason to translate this present participle, *hoi erchomai*, into the English word "coming," giving the reader the impression that this is an ever-increasing number of martyrs, with the group getting larger and larger as more and more martyrs find their way into Heaven (without being raptured) during the great tribulation, for the following reasons:

1. because the context determines the present participle;
2. and because this context clearly indicates this group is fixed in number.

Therefore, we may conclude that the group is complete in number, and is presently standing before the throne of God when John first beheld them.

Note: To justify this ever-growing multitude in the heavenlies, the pretribulationalists teach that this great multitude must represent Gentile martyrs that are saved during a tremendous Gentile revival that takes place during the seventieth week of Daniel. Again, using their own system of thinking, this position makes no sense whatsoever.

17-10

The pretribulational school of thought maintains that the church cannot be on earth during the seventieth week because the seventieth week is Jewish when once again God deals directly with Israel. Yet to explain away the great multitude, they teach the most incredible Gentile revival of all time will have to occur during a time when their system demands God has returned His emphasis back solely to Israel!

17-11

2 Thessalonians 2:4, 11,12 teaches that when Antichrist "takes his seat in the temple of God, displaying himself as being God . . . God will send upon them [the Gentile world] a deluding influence so that they might believe what is false, in order that they all may be judged who did not believe the truth, but took pleasure in wickedness."

17-12

There is absolutely no evidence in the book of Revelation of such a revival occurring at any time during the last days before the day of the Lord, and certainly none thereafter.

17-13

Since this group of men and women standing before the throne clothed in white robes and holding palm branches in their hands obviously have resurrected bodies, this great multitude can only be the raptured church — not the martyred fifth-seal souls who will not receive their resurrection bodies until the first day of the millennium.

17-14

The martyred saints seen under the throne at the fifth seal, will not be given their resurrection bodies until the very first day of the Millennium.

17-15

At the Great White Throne judgment after the Millennium.

17-16

Immediately, "in a moment, in the twinkling of a eye."

17-17

The great multitude arrives in Heaven immediately after the sign of the end of the age (the day of the Lord) is given at the sixth seal.

17-18

This multitude is made up of those "who come out of the great tribulation" (Revelation 7:14), when the great tribulation is "cut short" by Christ (Matthew 24:22).

17-19

The next event following the arrival of the great multitude in Heaven is the seventh seal (Revelation 8:1-6), the day of the Lord.

17-20

Both Christ and Paul taught that the Rapture will occur when the great tribulation is cut short, just before the day of the Lord.

17-21

Paul taught that the church and the dead in Christ will receive their resurrection bodies at the Rapture.

17-22

The great heavenly multitude has bodies.

17-23

Because this great multitude has bodies, it cannot represent the fifth-seal souls (great-tribulation martyrs), because they do not receive their resurrection bodies until the first day of the Millennium.

17-24

The only possible conclusion is that this great multitude must be both the "raptured church" and the "dead in Christ" for whom Christ "wast slain . . . from every tribe and tongue and people and nation."

17-25

Old and New Testament believers who had already died or would die before the Lord's return, a group that will definitely include Old Testament saints.

17-26

Isaiah 26:19-21; Joel 2:31,32a; and Daniel 12:1-3.

17-27

Isaiah and Joel teach that the Old Testament saints will be resurrected just before the day of the Lord while the great tribulation is in process, and Daniel's passage confirms the fact that the resurrection will follow "a time of distress such as never occurred since there was a nation until that time."

17-28

The seven trumpets described in the book of Revelation are all blown by angels (Revelation 8:6; cf. 11:15), not by God. Christians would have to endure the wrath of God in the six trumpet judgments which is contrary to God's promise in Romans 5:9 and 1 Thessalonians 1:10; 5:9.

17-29

The trumpet blown initiating the return of Israel from Assyria and Egypt after the seventieth week is complete, just before the millennial kingdom (Isaiah 27:12, 13).

17-30

Just prior to the overthrow of Antiochus Epiphanies.

17-31

The next time that God will blow the trumpet will be to announce the destruction of Antichrist. In the only two instances recorded of God's blowing the trumpet, in each case He blows the trumpet shortly after His holy Temple has been outrageously defiled, and just before He destroys the "defiler."

17-32

When the sign of the end of the age extinguishes the heavenly lights, and the sign of Christ's return fills the darkened universe with the glory of Christ, the angels of God will gather His elect from the four corners of the earth to meet the Lord in the air. Then, and only then, will the 144,000 persevering Jews (those who have kept themselves spiritually chaste during the first half of the seventieth week) be brought "into the bond of the covenant" described by Ezekiel.

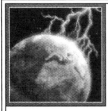

17-33

On their foreheads.

17-34

God's wrath is directly against *all* "the men who do *not* have the seal of God on their foreheads."

17-35

They are brought "into the bond of the covenant." In other words, this is when the 144,000 are brought into a saving relationship with their Messiah, Jesus Christ.

17-36

They will not be raptured with the church because they are not brought into the bond of the covenant until just after the church is raptured. On the other hand, they will become the "first fruits" unto Christ of unbelieving Israel. However, those of the nation of Israel, in general (those who initially support the covenant but nevertheless refused to give their allegiance to Antichrist and who refused to flee to the wilderness when given the chance) will be saved only after God's day-of-the-Lord refinement of them, after "the fullness of the Gentiles has come in" — that is, after the seventieth week is complete and God brings in "everlasting righteousness."

CHAPTER 18
THE DAY OF THE LORD

18-1

All passages dealing with the day of the Lord focus on but one event - the future day when God will unleash His wrath against the unrighteous in general and the beast empire nations of Antichrist in particular.

18-2

The day of the Lord will be that climactic event in history when God will pour out His wrath in judgment on the wicked world.

18-3

The heavens will pass away with a roar and the elements will be destroyed with intense heat, and the earth and its works will be burned up.

18-4

The phrase "the last days" (v. 3) is nowhere else used in Scripture in reference to the end of the Millennium, but is frequently used in relation to the Rapture (see, e.g., John 6:39,40,54), to the resurrection of the dead (John 11:24), and to the end of this present age (Acts 2:17; 2 Timothy 3:1) - all of which coincide with the day of the Lord at the second coming of Christ.

18-5

If Peter were speaking of a day of the Lord at the end of the Millennium, no one would be asking questions about Christ's coming (v. 4), because He would then be ruling over the earth as He had been for the previous thousand years.

18-6

If the "dual" day of the Lord position were correct, the day of the Lord at the second coming of Christ - the most traumatic event in history - would already have occurred a thousand years earlier, and no one during the Millennium would make the absurd comment that "all continues just as it was from the beginning of creation" (v. 4).

18-7

Peter's reference to the day of the Lord coming like a thief (v. 10) perfectly parallels Paul's day-of-the-Lord passage given in 1 Thessalonians 5:2-4, where he explains that "the times and the epochs" of the coming (*parousia*) of Christ will come like a thief.

18-8

Peter's illustrations about the Flood and the destruction of Sodom and Gomorrah (2:4-9; 3:6) are abbreviated versions of identical illustrations given by Christ in the Olivet Discourse, which deals with the wrath of Christ at His second coming (*parousia*).

18-9

In 3:15-16 Peter links his teaching on the day of the Lord, to the teaching of Paul on exactly the same issue. Paul never wrote about a day of the Lord at the end of the Millennium, but rather a day of the Lord that will occur at the coming of Christ (1 Thessalonians 4-5).

18-10

The day of the Lord will clearly be a judgment by fire.

18-11

"The heavens will pass away with a roar and the elements will be destroyed with intense heat, and the earth and its works will be burned up."

18-12

"According to His promise we are looking for new heavens and a new earth, in which righteousness dwells."

18-13

His end-time judgment will be entirely supernatural, administered directly by Himself, through His avenging angels (see Matthew 13:30, 39,40). It will not be executed through any human or natural means (Ezekiel 38:23 cf. Isaiah 2:17; Revelation 6:16,17). The entire world will know that the calamity upon earth is the judgment of God, not an offensive strike by a hostile government or an act of nature.

18-14

The seventh seal.
Note: As initially established in chapter 10, under the subtitle of "The Large Scroll," the large scroll cannot be opened until all seven seals are opened, first. As carefully explained in chapter 10 of this study guide, when the seventh and last seal is broken open by the "Lion of Judah," then the large scroll can be opened that initiates the wrath of God upon the earth's wicked, during a time known as "the day of the Lord."

18-15

The angels of God. It will be the angels of God who will harvest the earth by fire, at the end of the age (the day of the Lord).

18-16

He took the censer, filled it with fire, and threw it to the earth. It is a symbolic foreshadowing of God's fiery day-of-the-Lord judgment that is to immediately follow.

18-17

The first, second, third and sixth trumpet judgments.

18-18

The heavenly angels are the reapers.

18-19

The heavenly angels of God. It just again confirms the fact that the day of the Lord begins with the opening of the seventh seal, fitting right down to the finest detail, the description of this time of fiery judgment.

18-20

First, to judge the ungodly, and secondly, to purify Israel.

18-21

The wrath of God is the necessary consequence of man's blatant, unrepentant rebellion against a holy, loving God; and if we ignore or minimize the reality of God's wrath, we do so to our own eternal peril.

18-22

The day of the Lord (God's wrath) will be used to purify the nation Israel as He did the 144,000 in the Edomite wilderness.

18-23

"It will be darkness and not light, as when a man flees from a lion [the great tribulation of Antichrist], and a bear meets him [the day of the Lord] . . ."

18-24

It will be this remnant of the nation of Israel who supported the covenant with Antichrist but who refused to give their allegiance to him along with "the woman" that flees — the 144,000 first fruits of Israel — that will become the heart of His earthly millennial kingdom.

18-25

Ten percent!

18-26

The completion of the spiritual kingdom of God, bringing an end to the rule and kingdom of Satan.

18-27

Ultimately Christ will destroy Antichrist at the final battle of Armageddon (the last event of the day of the Lord), but first, "by the appearance of His coming [*parousia*]," Christ will render him helpless, as the first event of the day of the Lord.

18-28

The Greek word is *katargeo* which can legitimately be translated as "rendered useless." Christ will in effect "hand-cuff" Antichrist and his forces and "render him useless." This restriction of Antichrist's power will happen "at the appearance of His coming." In other words, when "every eye will see Him" (Rev. 1:7), when the church is gathered to Christ in the clouds and the wrath of God begins, Antichrist will be "rendered useless" until the time of final judgment and destruction, when he will be slain.

18-29

Those Jews who have escaped the persecution of Antichrist by hiding in remote areas of Israel will venture out to launch guerrilla attacks against the surrounding nations which have come against Israel in the valley of Jehoshaphat just before the day of the Lord begins. The strategy, in fact, will be much like the ancient resistance movement of Judas Maccabaeus against Antiochus Epiphanes in the second century B.C.

18-30

The martyrdom of the two witnesses, probably Moses and Elijah.

18-31

The world will rejoice, utterly deluded by diabolical belief that the end of those "troublemakers" will bring an end to the wrath of God they have been experiencing. By the death of the two witnesses, Antichrist will be deluded into thinking his rule is secure when in reality it is over and will, like the rest of the ungodly world, believe that his battle with the forces of God is finally won.

18-32

1. God will permit Antichrist to kill the two witnesses, and
2. to assemble his forces for his predetermined defeat at Armageddon, which is still to come thirty days later.

18-33

Three of the six issues (the bad news, so to speak) will be history. Then and not before,
(1) Israel's transgression against God will be finished,
(2) their sin against God will be ended, and
(3) full atonement for their iniquity will be satisfied before God (see Romans 11:11,12,25,26a).

18-34

1. The time of the Gentiles will be fulfilled, (the fullness of the Gentiles will have come in), and
2. Israel's sin will finally be atoned for.

CHAPTER 19
THE MYSTERY OF GOD IS FINISHED

19-1

The sweetness represents God's gracious redemption of Israel which will compete the spiritual kingdom of God, bringing in the physical kingdom of God over which Christ will rule.

19-2

The bitterness represents the final wrath of God, the worst ever to be poured out, that will be as swift as it is devastating upon the kingdom of darkness.

19-3

The close of the seventieth week will mark the close of the large scroll.

19-4

The "little scroll" — with its bittersweet contents — is a record of the events that occur *after* the seventieth week is complete.

19-5

1. Christ reclaims the nation of Israel that survives the seventieth week to Himself.
2. God Almighty reclaims the rule over earth from Satan.
3. Christ reclaims the physical possession of earth at the battle of Armageddon.

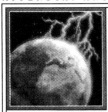

19-6

360 days.

19-7

(1) Regular sacrifice is abolished, and

(2) the abomination of desolation is set up.

Note: The solution lies in the simple fact that Daniel was referring to the "duration" of the abomination, not to the "interval" between the abolishing of the regular sacrifice and the setting up of the abomination. In other words, Antichrist's desecration of the Temple (by stopping the sacrifice and demanding the world's worship from "the holy place") will continue from the middle of the week - that is, from the point when Antichrist "puts a stop to sacrifice and grain offering" for 1,290 days "until a complete destruction, one that is decreed, is poured out on the one who makes desolate" (Daniel 9:27).

19-8

Thirty days after the seventieth week ends.

19-9

Antichrist will be destroyed on the last day of the thirty day period - exactly 1,290 days (three and one half years plus thirty days) after he desecrates the Temple by abolishing the sacrifice and demanding the world's worship at the mid-point of the seventieth week.

19-10

Israel as a nation will not "acknowledge their guilt and seek My face" (Hosea 5:15) until after the seventieth week is complete and the sins of Israel are atoned for (Daniel 9:24). After the seventieth week is complete, when "the fullness of the Gentiles has come in" (Romans 11:25), then God will "bring in everlasting righteousness" (Daniel 9:24).

19-11

After the completion of the seventieth week, when the sin of Israel has finally been atoned for, Israel will repent of her sin and three days later, she will be reunited spiritually and physically with her Messiah.

19-12

Then "they will look on Me whom they have pierced; and they will mourn." It will be a personal, face-to-face meeting with Jesus.

19-13

Christ once again literally returns to earth in physical form, descending to earth from the heavenly Zion for the face-to-face salvation of Israel.

19-14

This passage is speaking about the Jewish remnant that will "see" Christ when He literally comes down to earth for the second time, this time for the salvation of Israel, the first time being when Christ "offered [Himself] once to bear the sins of many" at His first coming.

19-15

For several reasons it seems certain that this "angel" is none other than Christ Himself when He physically comes back to earth for the spiritual salvation of Israel.

19-16

When we consider the context of the book of Revelation, we see in chapter 5 that only the Lamb of God, Christ (v.9) is worthy to open the scroll and break its seals. With this in mind, we then see that the "strong angel, coming down out of heaven . . . had in His hand a little book which was open." If Christ is the only one permitted to open the large scroll, it is highly probable that He will be the only one worthy to open the smaller scroll as well.

19-17

By Him who lives forever and ever.

19-18

Yes.

19-19

The "figure with appearance of a man" clearly refers to Christ, who had "the likeness of the glory of the Lord." The prophet later sees the same figure, described in almost exact the same way: "The hand of the Lord fell on me there. Then I looked, and behold, a likeness as the appearance of a man . . . "

19-20

The appearance of Christ in the book of Ezekiel parallels the appearance of the strong angel in Revelation 10.

19-21

Daniel 10:5,6, 16.

19-22

He "swore by Him who lives forever."

19-23

Both passages are in the context of the salvation of Israel, both referring to Christ's coming for their salvation, as a "roaring lion."

19-24

From heaven, to earth.

Note: The author recognizes that he has gone to some great lengths to show that John's "strong angel" is Christ, coming down to earth from heaven. Actually, in all my reading, no one has ever put all these issues together the way we have attempted to do in this chapter. For that reason I want you, the student, to have a strong biblical foundation for the incredible events that now occur during the next few days, immediately following the close of the seventieth week and the return of Christ to earth for the salvation of Israel. This is the one event Satan has done all in his power to prevent because with the salvation of the remnant of Israel that survives the seventieth week, approximately 10%. the spiritual kingdom of God will be complete, and God Almighty will reclaim the physical rule over earth, bringing an end to Satan and his kingdom of darkness. Therefore, let us now look at, in detail, the incredible events that unfold during the first six days after the close of the seventieth week.

19-25

Christ physically will come back to earth from the heavenly Zion (Rom. 11:26), and He will be going to earthly Zion (Isa. 59:20), bringing everlasting righteousness to the seventieth week survivors of Israel.

19-26

Christ will physically come back to earth — specifically to Edom. Christ will personally gather together the 144,000 (the first fruits of Israel) who were saved immediately after the rapture of the true church.

19-27

Christ is pictured coming from Edom in garments sprinkled with the lifeblood of those enduring His wrath that has already begun.

19-28

Bozrah. A capital of Edom.

19-29

Micah 2:12,13.

19-30

1. It mentions Christ's going "forth for the salvation of His people" - in other words, for the ultimate salvation of the nation Israel.

2. Next, Christ will "strike the head of the house of the evil to lay him [Antichrist] open from thigh to neck."

First the salvation of Israel and then the destruction of Antichrist.

19-31

The mystery is God's divine plan to bring the nation of Israel's spiritual blindness and alienation from God to an end precisely at His appointed time, which is not meant to be "until the fullness of the Gentiles has come in," that is, **after** the end of the seventy weeks of Gentile domination which He required of the nation as a penalty for their sin. Only then will God "**bring in** everlasting righteousness" (Daniel 9:24).

19-32

Although the hearts of most Jews were unprepared to receive Christ at His first coming, the hearts of the Jewish remnant will "eagerly await Him" when He comes the second time.

19-33

The mystery will be finished "in the days of the voice of the seventh trumpet, when he is about to sound." In other words, Israel is saved just before the seventh trumpet sounds. Because when the seventh trumpet sounds, God Almighty will reclaim His rightful rule over earth — which is the one event Satan has done all in his power to prevent. And since the seventh trumpet does not sound until after the two witnesses have been resurrected on the fourth day following the close of the seventieth week (Revelation 11:11,15), the timing of Israel's salvation given by John in the New Testament substantiates exactly the timing of Israel's salvation given by Hosea in the Old Testament.

19-34

On the third day after the close of the seventieth week. "He will revive us after two days; He will raise us up on the third day."

19-35

1. The "clans of Judah," a remnant of Israel who have not taken the mark of the beast, those who have instead have been fighting against the surrounding Gentile nations in the valley of Jehoshaphat, and

2. Jews who, like the clans of Judah, survived the initial onslaught of Antichrist and will return to Israel from the lands of Egypt and Assyria where they have been in hiding (Hosea 11:10, 11a).

19-36

"The highway of holiness"

19-37

"The unclean will not travel on it." And they (the remnant of Israel coming from Egypt and Assyria) will join the Lord with His great entourage marching triumphantly to Jerusalem.

19-38

"He [Christ — the "strong angel"] will roar like a lion."

19-39

"The house of David" will be the last portion of the nation Israel which "the Lord will save," which suggests that certain Jews who had initially hidden in the hills of Israel - all a part of "the compromised woman" - will have returned to Jerusalem after Christ appeared initially and incapacitated Antichrist.

19-40

The third day after the close of the seventieth week.

19-41

The spiritual kingdom of God will be complete, spelling certain doom to the kingdom of darkness and promising the physical kingdom of God upon earth will be turned over to Christ to rule.

19-42

The resurrection of the two witnesses, which causes the world to experience "great fear."

19-43

1. Their mission will be accomplished.

2. The seventieth week will be complete.

3. Antichrist's "authority to act" (Rev. 13:5) will be history.

4. The surviving remnant of Israel will all be saved.

5. Christ will be present personally to breathe life into their breathless bodies and send them "up into heaven in the cloud," where their enemies will behold them (Revelation 11:12).

19-44

During that very hour there will be a great earthquake, and a tenth of the city will fall, seven thousand people will be killed by the earthquake, and the rest will be terrified and give "glory to the God of heaven."

19-45

The sounding of the seventh trumpet. This event marks the point at which God Almighty reclaims divine authority over the earth from Satan, the great usurper and consumate enemy of God, the ruler over the kingdom of darkness.

19-46

The sounding of the seventh trumpet will most probably occur on the fifth day, following the completion of the seventieth week.

19-47

It is particularly important to note that "the kingdom of the world [will] become the kingdom of our Lord [God the Father], and of His Christ" immediately after the seventh trumpet is blown but before the beginning of the bowl judgments (i.e., before "the third woe" [Revelation 11:14]) that begins the final wrath of God.

19-48

Daniel 2:44 says that God will set up His kingdom (upon earth) before the hostile nations are destroyed.

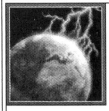

19-49

The deliverers will be on top of Mount Zion, and will more probably represent the 144,000 — the first fruits of Israel.

19-50

The 144,000 are shown on top of Mount Zion with Christ at the very same time in the sequence of end-time events as this event recorded in Obadiah 21 takes place.

19-51

"Thou King of the nations."

19-52

It is this particular psalm that is sung by Israel in connection with the Feast of Tabernacles when, once a year, they travel to the top of Mount Zion where the celebration is held even today. This feast which occurs exactly five days after the Day of Atonement is celebrated only on Mount Zion. Although Psalm 118 is used in the Feast of Tabernacles to represent God's protection during their forty-year wilderness sojourn and God's provision in the harvest, in reality this psalm is clearly prophetic, looking forward to the national salvation of Israel after undergoing great distress and the severe discipline of the Lord. **Note:** As an aside, it is interesting to note that the Feast of Tabernacles occurs on the summit of Mount Zion, exactly five days after Yom Kippur, the Day of Atonement. The parallels between the events of end-times and several of these critical Jewish holy days is incredible. Read the Epilogue of *The Sign* for a more in-depth discussion of this matter. The parallels one can make between the holy days and the end-times will not be gone into in depth in this study guide.

19-53

During that time of final wrath (Revelation 15:1), the newly-saved nation of Israel (although only a tenth part) will be divinely hidden and protected, probably for a little less than three weeks.

19-54

After He miraculously splits the Mount of Olives, the remnant will escape through the "valley of the mountains" to a place called Azel - a place whose location is not identified in Scripture and is only known by God.

19-55

After Christ returns to heaven, He will hold court at the divine "Bema-Seat" where all the elect who have been resurrected or raptured will be judged according to their faithfulness to God.

19-56

All of the elect, the entire spiritual kingdom of God including both Old and New Testament saints, who have been resurrected or raptured. Each will be judged according to their faithfulness to God.

19-57

Revelation 11:15-18. After rule over all earthly kingdoms will be returned to God Almighty (vv. 15b-17), and just prior to the destruction of "those who destroy the earth" (v. 18b).

CHAPTER 20
THE FINAL WRATH OF GOD

20-1

God will first establish His own indestructible kingdom and then He will utterly crush the end-times nations that oppose Him. In other words, the kingdoms of Antichrist (representing Satan's kingdom of darkness) will be destroyed after God has established His everlasting kingdom at the seventh trumpet.

20-2

1. The seventh trumpet is sounded (15a).
2. Almighty God reclaims His reign over the world (15b-17).
3. Still on earth after God's reign begins, the nations respond with rage (18a).
4. God pours out His wrath on the nations (18b).
5. The bema-seat judgment takes place (18c).
6. The time has come to destroy the nations (18d).
7. The preview to the bowl judgments is described (compare v. 19 with Rev. 15:5-8).

20-3

The Greek word translated "bowl" in Revelation refers to a shallow bowl or saucer, a radically different kind of container than a vial. The word is suggestive of rapidity in the emptying of the contents. This indicates that God's final judgment will be both swift and pervasive, which is the general understanding reflected in both the Old and New Testaments.

20-4

Isaiah 42:25; Jeremiah 10:25; Psalm 79:1-7; Zephaniah 3:8.

20-5

The heavenly temple is opened, and the ark of God's covenant is revealed.

20-6

(1) The salvation of Israel completing the spiritual kingdom of God, and
(2) the reclaiming of the rule over earth by God Almighty at the sounding of the seventh trumpet.

20-7

(1) The supreme symbol of God's covenant with Israel;
(2) Visible symbol of God's presence and was even referred to as the throne of God;
(3) Symbolized the power of God's presence when Israel went into battle;
(4) The ark was closely associated with the holiest day of the Jewish year, the Day of Atonement (Yom Kippur).

20-8

"Which are the last, because in them the wrath of God is finished"

20-9

Each judgment will come upon the earth quickly and completely, and the judgments seem to follow one another in rapid succession. Although the exact time and duration of the bowl judgments is not specified, all seven, along with the battle of Armageddon, must transpire within a time frame that is less than four weeks in total.

20-10

Although the final wrath of God, the bowl judgments, and Armageddon will be against the world in general, the last three bowl judgments and the battle of Armageddon will, in part, single out the beast empire nations which under the direction of Antichrist will have brutalized Israel in the last days.

20-11

The first bowl will bring loathsome sores on those who have taken the mark of Antichrist and worshipped him.

20-12

The second bowl will be poured in the sea, causing it to become like the blood of a dead man.

20-13

The third bowl will pollute all the rivers and springs, causing those bodies of water also to become like blood.

20-14

The fourth bowl will scorch all ungodly men with intense heat.

20-15

The fifth bowl will bring total darkness on the evil earthly kingdom of Antichrist, causing men to "gnaw their tongues because of pain."

20-16

All these excruciating afflictions will not bring men to repentance, the opportunity for which they will have forfeited when they took the mark of Antichrist.

20-17

The ungodly nations of the "whole world," under the leadership of Antichrist, will be preparing Satan's desperate last-chance battle against God - the "Armageddon Campaign" of Antichrist. To bring them more quickly to their ultimate destruction, God will assist Satan's forces by drying up the Euphrates River, giving the wicked kings in the East more rapid access to Israel.

20-18

This will be the most severe judgment of God, not only upon the nations of the final beast empire, but upon the whole world in general. First, the world will undergo the worst earthquake known to man. And then, in the midst of this worldwide chaos, hundred-pound hailstones will climax the devastation brought on by the earthquakes. The cities will have already been leveled; homes, apartments, and the like will lie in ruins, offering little protection, if any, to those who survive the earthquakes. And then will come the hail . . .

20-19

"The great city" which is a reference to Jerusalem (see Revelation 11:8) and "Babylon the great," a reference to the city that will identify with the Babylonian Harlot during the end times.

20-20

The earthquakes associated with the seventh bowl judgment which will split the city of Jerusalem in three parts, will actually be the destruction of Mount Zion upon which the city sets.

20-21

The marriage of the Lamb.

20-22

It is commonly thought that Christ's bride will consist only of the true church, but careful study of the Old as well as the New Testament clearly indicates that His bride will include all the saints, the redeemed of Israel as well as the church — in other words, the same group that was raptured and resurrected on the same day that God's wrath began, the same group that has just been rewarded for their faithfulness at the bema seat of Christ. I.e., the spiritual kingdom of God that resides with Christ in heaven.

20-23

Hosea 2:19,20; Isaiah 54:5-8; Romans 4:11; Ephesians 5:23,24; Hebrews 11:9-10, 16.

20-24

The heavenly city that God has prepared for Abraham and all his spiritual descendants can be none other than the same heavenly city He has prepared for the true church — that is, the New Jerusalem — because, like all other believers, the true church is among the spiritual descendants of Abraham.

20-25

Only one. Scripture nowhere speaks, or even hints, of two classes of believers, two heavenly households, two heavenly cities, or two brides of Christ. There is only one kingdom of God and only one King, Jesus Christ. Citizens of that kingdom who lived before Christ was crucified and resurrected are just as much saved by the redeeming blood of Christ as believers who live after He came to earth as God incarnate.

20-26

Christ will come back to earth with His army of angels (His reapers) to defeat the remainder of the ungodly forces on earth (at the battle of Armageddon), thereby reclaiming physical possession of the earth.

20-27

The identity of these "armies . . . in heaven" (Revelation 19:14) is not made explicit in the text, but when this is examined in light of other Scriptures it seems there can be no question, in this writer's opinion, as to their identity. In the parable of the wheat and the tares, Christ Himself states that "the harvest is the end of the age; and the reapers are angels" (Matthew 13:39) as Christ explains in verses 40-43a.

In addition, Christ specifically taught His disciples that "the son of Man is going to come in the glory of His Father with His angels; and will then [with His angels] recompense every man according to his deeds" (Matt. 16:27).

20-28

Isaiah 34:1-3 and Ezekiel 39:1-5, 12, 13.

20-29

Daniel 2:44 and 7:9, 11.

20-30

First the kingdom of God will be "set up" (at the sounding of the seventh trumpet), and then God's final wrath will totally destroy Antichrist and the final beast empire of Satan. And thus with the defeat of Antichrist, Christ will forever reclaim the physical possession of earth for the physical kingdom of God.

20-31

They are thrown "alive" into the lake of fire which burns with brimstone.

20-32

In a seeming discrepancy, Ezekiel speaks of Antichrist (Gog) being buried in Hamon-gog with the multitude of his army, where as in Revelation 19 he is shown being cast alive with the false prophet into the lake of fire. There is no doubt in this author's mind that both these passages refer to Antichrist.

20-33

Yes. Isaiah 11:4; 2 Thessalonians 2:8.

20-34

This powerful world ruler will be buried, but more importantly he "will be cast out of [his] tomb like a rejected branch" (v. 19). In other words, Antichrist "the man" will not remain buried in his own tomb like the other "kings of nations" who "lie in glory," but instead will be "cast out of his tomb," as it were, "like a rejected branch" (vv. 18,19) - being cast alive into the lake of fire.

This corresponds to Revelation 20:4,5 where John again uses a derivative of the same Greek word translated "alive" directly in reference to the resurrection bodies received by the martyrs at the "first resurrection."

20-35

Most probably Magog will be the leading nation of the three-nation power base that Antichrist will use to lead his ten-nation confederacy of the final beast empire of Satan. God will specifically destroy Magog with fire.

20-36

The nation of Edom has always been the enemy of God, going back to the time of Jacob and Esau. "Because you have had everlasting enmity and have delivered the sons of Israel to the power of the sword at the time of their calamity, at the time of punishment of the end," Edom will be dealt with in a unique way after the final battle of Armageddon. Edom will be "utterly destroyed" and will become a memorial where "its smoke shall go up forever."

20-37

The day of the Lord.

CHAPTER 21
THE RESTORATION PERIOD

21-1

The restoration period is a forty-five-day period of time revealed in the book of Daniel (12:11,12). First there will be a thirty-day period immediately following the seventieth week of Daniel. Then there is an additional forty-five day period which takes place immediately after the thirty-day period and immediately before the Millennium begins (1,260 + 30 + 45 = 1,335). Thus we see that the 1,335 day total is achieved by adding together the 1,260 days (the last half of the seventieth week) plus the thirty-day reclamation period plus an additional forty-five day restoration period, extending right up to the first day of the Millennium.

21-2

1. The restoration of Mount Zion which was split into three parts at the final bowl judgment.
2. The restoration of Israel back to her own land, the land promised to Abraham more than four thousand years ago.
3. Christ will receive the reign over the earth from God the Father Almighty. When the rule upon earth is restored back to its rightful King.

21-3

(1) A time when the Temple will be restored on the summit of God's holy mountain, and
(2) A time when Gentile survivors will be brought to God's holy mountain.

21-4

At the seventh bowl judgment, "the mountains were not found" and "the great city [Jerusalem] was split into three parts."

21-5

The original Greek does not include the definite article and for that reason should really read "mountains were not found." In other words, with the absence of the definite article, it is safe to say that not all the mountains were leveled, but indeed, many were. Re. Ezekiel 39:4, simply translated, that means that whatever mountains were leveled by the seventh bowl judgment, it did not include the mountains where the final battle of Armageddon would be fought.

21-6

The mountains around the city of Jerusalem were definitely leveled by the seventh bowl earthquakes, including Mount Zion.

21-7

"All the land will be changed into a plain . . . "

21-8

Mount Zion must "be established as the chief of the mountains, and will be raised above the hills . . ."

21-9

"A very high mountain"

21-10

Israel will be restored back to her holy land . . . indeed fulfilling God's covenant with Abraham more than four thousand years ago. During this time Israel will return to the land — not in unbelief, not in self-reliance, not in defiance, not shaking her fist at God — but this time **in belief**.

21-11

"They shall come and shout for joy on the height of [Mt.] Zion."

21-12

They will be primarily those who have been divinely protected by the Lord, safely hidden in a place called "Azel" (Zechariah 14:5) during the final battle of Armageddon with its unimaginable devastation.

21-13

In some way not fully explained in Scripture, God will bring the survivors of those nations of the world to God's holy mountain in the land of Israel. This will include all those who have survived the trumpet judgments, those who have survived the bowl judgments, plus the few who survive the final battle of Armageddon.

21-14

The restoration of the Temple on the very summit of Mount Zion.

21-15

The millennial Temple will be the throne room in which Christ not only "will dwell among the sons of Israel forever" but from which He will rule over the nations of the earth - that is, over all those peoples who will survive both the day of the Lord and the Sheep and Goat judgment of Christ on the first day of the Millennium.

21-16

Christ Himself, not the redeemed Jews, will build the final Temple.

21-17

1. The entire top of the mountain is holy (Isaiah 43:12).
2. In the middle of this holy area on the top of Mount Zion will be "the sanctuary, the most holy place" (Isaiah 45:2, 3).
3. South of the summit, down the mountain a ways, will be the new city of Jerusalem (Isaiah 40:2 cf. 48:15), rebuilt by "My people Israel" who are restored from captivity (Amos 9:14 cf. Isaiah 58:12; 61:4).
4. And, "on the one side and on the other [side] of the holy allotment and of the property of the city . . . shall be [property] for the prince" (Isaiah 48:21).

21-18

David.

21-19

This will be the return of Christ back to heaven in preparation for receiving everlasting dominion over "all peoples, nations and men of every language" from God Almighty.

21-20

Afterwards.

21-21

The 45-day restoration period.

21-22

Christ's "kingdom will be an everlasting kingdom, and all dominions will serve and obey Him."

CHAPTER 22
THE MILLENNIUM BEGINS

22-1

A one thousand year period of time.

22-2

On the earthy level, the Millennium might be likened to the earth at the time of Adam and Eve in the Garden of Eden. The physical nature of God's creation will be brought back to its original perfection and the inter-relationship of all created life will once again be peaceful.

22-3

This can only refer to that time when Christ will literally return to earth in the end times to establish a literal kingdom encompassing the entire earth over which He will rule as King of Kings and Lord of Lords.

22-4

David will rule solely over Israel, whereas Christ will rule supremely over all the earth (including Israel) from His throne in the Temple which Christ shares with the Father in the center of the great and expansive holy area on the summit of Mount Zion.

22-5

There will be Gentile nations during the thousand years and each will, presumably, have its own king or ruler and its own particular governmental organization - all under the world rule of Christ.

22-6

The other nations of the world not only will serve and glorify God, but they will also serve His chosen nation Israel, rather than afflict them as they had for thousands of years.

22-7

1. Satan is bound.
2. The sheep and goat judgment of Christ.
3. The resurrection of the "beheaded" tribulation martyrs.
4. The new heavens and earth.
5. The descent of the New Jerusalem, the bride, down to earth.

22-8

Satan will be bound and thrown into the abyss for a thousand years.

22-9

The Sheep and Goat Judgment will separate the true citizens of the kingdom of God from the citizens of the kingdom of darkness.

22-10

The Lord makes clear that He will personally conduct the judgment from His throne on Mount Zion.

22-11

"All the angels [will be] with Him" which would seem to indicate that the angels (who have been His reapers during the day of the Lord) will again be part of this final judgment.

22-12

"All nations [peoples] will be gathered before" Christ to undergo judgment.

22-13

No. Only people of Gentile ancestry. *Ethnos* was a term used by Jews to refer to any non-Jewish people.

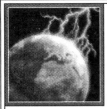

22-14

1. The first consideration will be whether or not the non-Jewish survivors of the day of the Lord have worshiped the beast or his image or have taken his mark. For those who fail this simple test - if indeed any do survive the day of the Lord - their condemnation will have already been established (Revelation 14:9-11), and the second test will be unnecessary.
2. The second consideration - applicable to those who have not worshiped the beast or his image - will be their individual treatment of Israel (Matthew 25:40).

22-15

As would be expected, the witnesses at this trial (as it was during the Holocaust trials) will be the survivors of Israel themselves — the very people that the world has so long ridiculed and persecuted. God then declares that "you [Israel] are my witnesses."

22-16

No. The ultimate basis for salvation of the "sheep" as they stand before Christ on the first day of the Millennium is not founded on works. The Scriptures teach without exception that salvation is by grace alone, through faith alone, solely in response to God's sovereign election before the foundation of the world (Ephesians 1:4-5; 2:8-9).

22-17

Christ tells the sheep to "inherit the kingdom prepared for you from the foundation of the world."

22-18

It is the opinion of this writer, although we cannot be adamant, that these are the martyrs who have died by "beheading" and are seen under the throne of God at the fifth seal. But for some reason those faithful witnesses who die before the Son of Man comes will not receive their resurrection bodies at the Rapture of the Church (when "the dead in Christ rise first") but later, on the first day of the Millennium.

22-19

No. Noted Greek scholar, Dr. Robert Gundry, says: "The parallelism of the aorist verbs in this passage, for sitting, giving, living and reigning, indicate actions that take place at the same time. Naturally it is the context which determines the time referred to by these verbs, clearly at the beginning of the Millennium because the passage in question ends with 'and they came to live [aorist tense] and reigned [aorist tense] with Christ for a thousand years,' thus defining exactly when the action takes place."

22-20

The first resurrection refers to the general resurrection of all believers "unto life."

22-21

The second resurrection is "a resurrection of judgment," which is really "the second death."

22-22

First phase, the resurrection of Christ, Himself.
Second phase, the resurrection of the "dead in Christ" — Old and New Testament saints at the Rapture.
Third phase, the resurrection of the "beheaded" martyrs on the first day of the Millennium.
Fourth phase, of sorts, of the first resurrection as well, when the believing men and women who go into the Millennium receive their resurrection bodies.
Note: The author believes that Revelation 20:7-14 is merely a parenthesis explaining the "second death" introduced in the preceding verse and referred to again at the end of verse 14, where it will occur for all unbelievers at the Great White Throne at the end of the Millennium.

22-23

The earth will be in a state of total devastation when the battle of Armageddon is over and the day of the Lord is completed.

22-24

In Isaiah 65:17-19 the order is explicit: first the new heavens and new earth (verse 17) and then the millennial kingdom (verse 19). The same sequence is seen again in the next and final chapter of Isaiah (Isaiah 66:22,23), first the new heavens and new earth (verse 22) and then events that will only occur during the millennial kingdom (verse 23).

22-25

The Greek term translated "new" (*kainos*) does not refer to something that has never existed before, but rather to the renewing of something that already exists.

22-26

The New Jerusalem, the heavenly mansions prepared for the bride of Christ, in brilliant beauty beyond anything we can imagine, will descend from heaven.

22-27

(1) We will be with the Lord forever in the most intimate kind of relationship.
(2) There will be "no temple in [the New Jerusalem], for the Lord God, the Almighty, and the Lamb, are its temple."
(3) We will be the bride of Christ, having been married already to Christ after the Rapture and resurrection during the reclamation period.

22-28

The Temple.

22-29

On the top of Mount Zion.

22-30

When the New Jerusalem descends from heaven, it will hover directly above the earth, with its center encompassing the newly built Temple on top of Mount Zion.

22-31

The Temple of God will therefore be the focal point both of the New Jerusalem and of the entire earth. In other words, Christ will rule over earth from His throne room in the new Temple, which will be an inseparable part of the New Jerusalem. . . . as they (the Lamb and His bride) dwell together in God's holy city, the New Jerusalem, in the midst of the kingdom of God upon earth.

22-32

This is true because if the New Jerusalem, the dwelling place of Christ's bride, were to remain in heaven during the Millennium while Christ is ruling on the earth, then He and His saints would be separated from each other throughout the thousand years, directly contradicting the two divine promises given above.

22-33

The marriage supper of the Lamb (Revelation 19:9 cf. Isaiah 25:6-8).

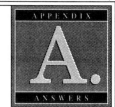

22-34

The bride of Christ will, of course, be there, "adorned for her husband" (Revelation 21:2) - that is, the raptured and resurrected saints from all ages. But there will also be invited guests in addition to the bride (Revelation 19:9). These will include those who have come to faith in Christ after the day of the Lord begins - those who survive the great tribulation by Antichrist, the day of the Lord's wrath, and the Sheep and Goats Judgment.

22-35

All who are "overcomers" shall inherit these things.